JACK
LONDON

*The
Pursuit
of a
Dream*

BY THE AUTHOR

Willa: The Story of Willa Cather's Growing Up

Stephen Crane: The Story of an American Writer

Jack London: The Pursuit of a Dream

Hannah Herself

Jack
London

THE PURSUIT OF A DREAM

BY RUTH FRANCHERE

THOMAS Y. CROWELL COMPANY
New York

12253
921

to JOAN LONDON MILLER

Chapter **1**

A bell sounded overhead, and at once the murky water beneath the huge side-wheels of the ferry steamer *Bay City* began to billow and churn. The vessel, as though wakened from deep slumber, shook herself and reluctantly settled down to steady grumbling. Crew members called to each other; a gate clanked into place. As the ferry slowly crawled out into the spanking water of San Francisco Bay, passengers who had been standing about in drowsy, early morning stupor, stirred themselves and headed for the upper cabin.

At the rail near the stern a young sailor remained alone, his powerful, short legs spread wide, a battered sou'wester planted firmly on the back of his mop of curly light brown hair. Obviously he was no tender commuter, headed for a job across the bay. The deep-bronzed skin of his face and throat told of daily assaults by wind, sun, and salt spray; his worn, run-over boots

1

spoke of months of duty beyond the relative shelter of San Francisco Bay and the deck of a ferryboat. Calloused, scarred hands, and bulging muscles that strained at the seams of his oilskin jacket marked him as a boy who had pulled and hauled the sheets and tackle of one of the many ships that sailed in and out of the Golden Gate during these late years of the nineteenth century.

If any one of the passengers had asked, he would have put him straight at once. "Jack London," he might have said, his full mouth spreading in its wide, amiable smile that unself-consciously revealed the absence of two front teeth. "Able seaman. Fresh off the three-masted sealing ship, *Sophia Sutherland*. Seven months at sea along the coast of Japan and up into the Bering Sea." He would gladly have gone on to recount grand tales of adventure aboard the *Sophie,* as he liked to call her, until the ferry entered the slip at Oakland, California, and he stepped off onto the soil of his home town.

But on this morning in September, 1893, no one spoke to him and so his mind was not drawn from the troubled thoughts that held him to the deck of the *Bay City.* Though he had not slept all night, his head was clear as his eyes swept the slowly receding skyline of San Francisco. Back there somewhere, in saloons and dives, were his friends of seven months—Axel, Victor, Red John, Long John, and the others, still reeling from a long night of celebration. In spite of all their resolu-

2

tions made continuously during the thirty-seven sober days of the homeward journey from Yokohama, they had been caught in the net that ensnared them every time they set foot on land. In two or three days, the saloonkeepers and boardinghouse harpies would have the last of their pay and they would be shanghaied onto any ship that wanted seamen.

Jack London shook himself as though to ward off the invisible net that might have caught him, too, if he had not had a home to go to, or perhaps a stronger will to start the new life that they had all talked of on the homeward run. He crammed his hands into his pockets and fingered the gold pieces that the paymaster had turned over to him. He still had them. Or most of them. He alone, seventeen years old and the youngest of the crew, had escaped!

A momentary flush of pride was checked by thoughts of his lost friends. He would never sail with them again, he knew, and they would never settle down to any other life. Axel and Red John would never see their aging parents in Norway and Sweden as they had planned. Long John would not go to a navigation school to study to be a captain. All would end their lives as common seamen, laboring day and night with nothing to look forward to but a few days of carousing in port at the end of each run.

Suddenly, Jack spread his arms wide and flexed his powerful muscles, feeling them ripple under his jacket.

And then a great smile of contentment lighted his handsome, boyish face.

"Not this sailor," he muttered into the wake of the steamer. "This one has other plans."

With one quick catlike movement he tossed his canvas sea bag to his shoulder, whirled about, and bounded toward the steps to the upper deck. A few leaps, and he was at the top, striding with his sure rolling gait toward the bow. Out on the forward deck in front of the pilot house, he dropped his sea bag at his feet and leaned against the rail. At once all thought of the *Sophia Sutherland* and her crew left him. He was at home.

Shielding his eyes from the glare of the east sun on the rippling water of the great bay, he searched for all the landmarks that he knew so well. They were passing Goat Island now, and he smiled, recalling a morning when he was about eleven or twelve. He pressed a finger to his forehead, trying to remember.

Yes, he decided, it must have been a Saturday. He had just finished selling the last of his newspapers, no school bell called, and his Saturday job on the ice wagon had not yet started. As usual he had read himself to sleep the night before—some wonderful yarn about the sea—and as usual his mother had pulled him from bed almost before daylight, complaining about the light that was still burning and about the way he was ruining his health reading all those library books that he carried home by the armload.

4

Scarcely opening his eyes, he had pulled on some ragged old clothes, swallowed his breakfast, and staggered out the door. Every morning was the same. Papers must be sold; the money must be brought home to his mother.

But on this particular morning, something special must have happened. Perhaps the sea story that he had been reading made him bold, or maybe an especially enticing breeze from the bay caused him to rebel against the drudgery and monotony of his life in which there was seldom any time for play.

Swiftly he made up his mind, and as swiftly he went into action. He remembered stealing back into the kitchen after his papers were sold, wrapping some lunch in newspaper, snatching books and fishing pole from his room, and slipping out again. As though chased by the demon that his mother would have been had she caught him, he raced all the way to the sheltered estuary and threw himself into the little barnacle-encrusted skiff that he and his father sometimes used for a few stolen hours of fishing.

Breathless, he shoved off and hoisted the tattered sail. The breeze caught it, and without a moment's hesitation he headed toward the open bay.

As he stood out on the deck of the *Bay City* on this September morning, Jack London, able seaman, sensed again the ecstasy of that stolen day in his young life some five or six years before. Clutching the tiller firmly, he remembered, he had set his course for far-off Goat Island. He could almost feel the welcome salt spray on his hot face and the tug of the swift current against his small craft. Triumphantly he had made it to the leeward side of the island, where he dropped anchor and spent a blissful day of fishing and reading his books of high adventure.

It was past sundown when he crept into the kitchen to placate his mother with a huge string of rock cod and the coins from the papers he had sold in the early morning. No amount of scolding could spoil the joyful secret day, though he did vow again, as he rolled into bed, that sometime he would run away to sea.

That was only the first of many days on the bay, though none had ever surpassed it in pure delight and satisfaction.

Abruptly, Jack shifted his gaze and his thoughts. To the north he could make out the shadowy form of Point Pablo that marked the entrance to San Pablo Bay. How many times he had skimmed that point in his later wild bay-roaming days on his own sloop, the *Razzle Dazzle,* and later on the *Reindeer,* living to the full the adventurous life that he had read so much about. To the south, in the lower bay, lay the oyster beds that he and other young waterfront pirates had raided on many a moonless night. Those were not good days and nights to remember, but they had been part of his experience. From that life, to escape the inevitable downward drift and sordid end that many of his rough companions had already succumbed to, he had signed on the *Sophia Sutherland*.

Jack smiled as his thoughts sorted through those last days in Oakland. For the first time, he remembered, his mother had seemed relieved that he was leaving home even though, for seven months, he would not be contributing to the family purse. And who could blame her?

As the ferry churned steadily eastward, the wide expanse of the Oakland waterfront came more clearly into his view. He knew every foot of it, and as he gazed with eyes washed clear by seven months at sea, his boyhood seemed spread out before him on those ugly Oakland flats, the poorest, roughest area of the city.

Oh, he had lived in plenty of other places, he reminded himself, for his mother could never stay in one house for long. Eliza, his older stepsister, had told him about some of the earliest ones. But he, himself, could well remember at least half a dozen that they had lived in before they came finally to Oakland. Could he ever forget the constant packing and moving from one to another—a truck farm in Alameda—potato land on the bleak, foggy coast south of San Francisco—a fruit ranch near Livermore? The terror of empty houses and the loneliness of new ones would haunt him forever.

Jack heaved a long sigh and brushed a hand across his eyes, but the pictures kept tumbling through his mind. When he was almost eleven, after trying several neighborhoods in East Oakland, his mother had decided that they must move again. Perhaps one of her many schemes for making money had failed, or maybe she had again put all their savings into lottery tickets and lost. This time, the old wagon loaded with all their goods had carried them to this poorest area of Oakland, near The Point and the railroad track.

The ferry was crawling slowly now as she entered the inner harbor—the narrow estuary between Oakland and Alameda. Soon he could almost see it as he had seen it on that day—a small boy perched on top of the stack of boxes and barrels—a neighborhood of shacks and shanties. Their small weathered house on Pine Street had stood out only a little better than those about it. But by this time, he remembered, one home or another hadn't mattered. He had lived in too many to care very deeply any longer. Home was a place to sleep and eat in, to bring his earnings to, to escape from whenever he could.

The times that stood out in his memory, as he looked back now, were those too few hours he had spent near the water or on it. Sometimes he and his gentle, quiet father had stolen away to fish and sail the little skiff along the shore of the estuary among cargo vessels from all over the world. How they had talked and speculated and pondered while fish tugged at their lines, unheeded! To what distant ports had these strange and fascinating ships sailed? What exotic cargo had they carried in their holds?

Times like these had made the little Pine Street house seem not so bad, after all. Not bad until dusk.

Pictures. Pictures. As the *Bay City* moved slowly along toward her berth at the foot of Broadway, they flashed through his mind, telescoping the years into a brief span. Here on the waterfront in lower Oakland, he saw himself, again a small boy, waving good-by to his gray-bearded father, stooped and tired, as he set off each evening for the ferry landing to begin his dreary, night-long job as watchman. Saw himself hiding while his little dwarflike mother, dressed in black bonnet and rusty black dress, searched for him through her thick, steel-rimmed spectacles and then impatiently set out for one of the many spiritualist meetings that the neighborhood women doted on. Saw himself dash out of the house to roam the streets alone, look in at dance halls and bowling alleys, listen to the talk of sailors, watch in awe the gangs of older boys who seemed to be enjoying life in their rough way, making their own laws of the street.

Sometimes on Saturday nights, he remembered, if he had saved enough pennies from the ten that his mother allowed him to keep each week, or if he had collected enough junk from around the waterfront to sell to one of the junkmen, he had paid his way into the gallery of the old Opera House. *East Lynne!* And on one memorable night, *The Mikado!*

A smile twitched the corners of Jack's lips as he saw himself—small, shy, ragged little boy—exploring, listening, learning, absorbing everything good or bad that he came in contact with.

From the deck of the ferry Jack's eager eyes roamed on, while the pictures came faster now. Over there to the right, at the foot of Webster Street, he spied the little First and Last Chance saloon, and smiled as he remembered. Even at this early hour, Johnny Heinold would be inside, dressed in a clean white coat, polishing glasses, jotting down accounts in his little book.

For a moment Jack thought of stopping in to see him. But he shook his head resolutely. No. Stopping in would mean treats all around and more treats.

I'm through with that, he vowed again. Through for good.

But going to Johnny Heinold's was an important part of any homecoming, and he gave up the idea with regret.

The landing whistle, announcing the arrival of the *Bay City* at the Oakland ferry dock, scarcely disturbed Jack's reveries. That piercing hoot, so much a part of his young life, only sharpened his memories.

He was back in his paper-carrying days—back to a cold morning when rain had lashed at him as he walked his route, soaking him to the skin. Teeth chattering, he had pushed open the door of the First and Last Chance and had crept inside where the round stove glowed with warmth, where glasses and bottles gleamed and the fragrance of the free lunch at the bar twitched his nostrils. He remembered sliding along the wall toward a round table in the corner and slipping into a chair.

Johnny Heinold had often laughed with him, in the years that followed, over the rainsoaked little urchin that he had spied in the corner of his saloon. But for Jack, the day was never to be forgotten. Big-voiced men in sleek oilskin jackets had dried his coat in front of the stove, fed him from the free lunch slices of spicy sausage on delicious crunchy bread, and bought the last of his sodden, worthless newspapers.

Warmth and friendliness in a cold world, a door to adventure, that's what Johnny Heinold's means to me, Jack told himself as he tossed his sea bag to his shoulder and moved with the crowd of commuters toward the lower deck of the *Bay City*.

As he left the ferry dock and swung up Broadway for a few blocks, he glanced furtively around, torn between the desire to see some of the old crowd again and the more urgent wish to get past this part of town and into the new life that he planned for himself. A year ago he had known half the waterfront loafers of Oakland. Ahead, he thought he recognized a familiar figure and quickly cut across the rutted, dusty street to the other side, while he pulled a creased letter from his pocket and unfolded it. It was a message from Eliza that had been held for him in Yokohama, telling him that his parents had moved again to a house near her own.

". . . at 1321 East Twenty-second Avenue," he read aloud, his forehead crinkling in a little frown as he tried to recall just where that was. It was in the cotton mill area, he knew, and not far from his first school in Oakland—Garfield School—where he had learned to use his fists. But all the houses in that area were so much alike that he couldn't be sure which was now his.

No matter, he told himself. It'll be just another house.

The one thing that *did* matter was that he would be nearly two miles from the old neighborhood with all its associations. A faint smile flickered across his face as he wondered if perhaps his mother had a reason, this time, for moving from West to East Oakland. His mother was a determined woman.

Jack slipped the letter back into his pocket and gave himself over to the pleasure of walking along the oak-shaded streets of his home town at last, and to the strange problem of finding footing on a planked walk that seemed to rise and fall under his boots. A sailor on dry land, but the swell and rhythm of the sea were still in his bones. For a moment he thought of going on up to the library on Fourteenth Street to pick up some books to read, but he decided to wait until his feet could find the steps without stumbling.

As Jack turned his face eastward, his stride became steadier, and by the time he crossed the creek, his wide sailor gait was carrying him swiftly home. East Twenty-second Avenue . . . 1321 . . . There it was, a plain box of a house.

He hesitated a moment before he turned in. His father's face would light up with joy at the sight of his "Johnny." This he could always depend on. And his mother?

12

Wouldn't she be glad to have him, too, with gold pieces in his pocket?

Of one thing he could be sure. All of them—mother, father, and Eliza—would want to hear the stories he could tell of seven months at sea!

Chapter **2**

"You should've heard that wind in the rigging. Why, it rumbled like a train going across the trestle. The *Sophie* creaked and groaned and there I was, rolled up in my bunk trying to get some sleep."

Jack threw back his head and laughed. "Me, not able to sleep! You know it must have been a bad blow, Ma, if I couldn't sleep. And me just off the first watch."

His mother made a wry face, crinkling the corners of her little eyes behind her thick glasses. "Don't I know," she said dryly. "Never saw the morning when I didn't have to strip the covers off you and drag you out of bed. Sleep!"

His father's quiet voice interfered. "He was just a boy then, Flora. Never did get enough. Up at three o'clock to carry papers . . ."

Flora London snorted and banged the skillet on the old stove top. "Never got enough, either, when he was goose-chasing on the creek or running around all night with that wild bunch of hoodlums."

Eliza Shepard turned from the rusty iron sink, a dish towel in her hand. Her eyes strayed over the strong, handsome face and husky shoulders of her stepbrother. Nothing Jack ever did was wrong. He was only Jack— the boy she had cared for and loved since he was a baby.

"Go on, Jack," she urged. "What happened then?"

"Well, I guess I was just dropping off after all when the call came roaring down from the fo'c's'l. 'All hands on deck and shorten sail!' It was two bells in the middle watch, but we rolled out of our bunks and jumped into our oilskins, I tell you!"

Jack's voice went on, spinning out another of the stories that he had been telling nearly every evening at the kitchen table since he had come home from sea. How they had all laughed, even his mother, when he told of hiding a clammy, skinned seal in Long John's bunk. A howl like the one that shook the forecastle when Long John leaped from the bunk had echoed up and down the street that night.

At last, at nine o'clock, when Eliza reluctantly put on her coat to go to her own home nearby, she voiced the question that had been hanging in the air all during the evening. "Did you—did you find anything today, Jack?" she asked.

Jack frowned. Every night one of them asked. He knew what they were thinking. The gold pieces that he had brought home were gone—used to pay family debts and buy food. His father was old and ill, with little more than his small Civil War pension to live on. *He* was young and husky.

Couldn't they understand that he needed time to look around? He was starting a new life. A job with a chance to work up was what he wanted. More reading and study. Maybe night school.

But he brushed aside his irritation, grinned, and flexed the muscles of his arms and shoulders. "See those?" he boasted. "I don't have to take a kid's job any longer. A man-sized job for me. If I find the right thing, some day I'll be the boss."

But no one else smiled.

His father shook his gray head and stroked his beard. "These are bad times, Johnny. Haven't you seen the lines of men at every shop and factory? They queue up in the night so they'll be first in the morning if anybody's hiring. Why, they say there are three million people hunting for jobs in this country—any kind of work so it'll keep their families from starving. You can't be choosy these days, Son."

"I heard Hickmott hired a few extras yesterday," Eliza murmured.

"Hickmott!" Jack leaped from his chair and swung a clenched fist through the air, sending a cup flying into a corner of the kitchen. The crash of shattered crockery was his answer.

"Hickmott's Cannery!" In his eyes gleamed his hatred of that filthy old stable converted into a cannery, the torment of a year when he was fifteen, bound to the roaring, flashing machines for twelve, fifteen, eighteen hours a day. Once he had worked for thirty-six hours straight while his young brain reeled and he strained every nerve to keep his failing fingers from contact with the sharp, whirring machines. Ten cents an hour! But he had been lucky. There were youngsters of eight or nine working for thirty cents a day. Youngsters who were maimed for life by the flying machines.

He folded his arms across his chest and glowered at his sister. "I'll go back to sea first!"

"What'll that get you?" his mother snapped.

"Gold, that's what. And clean salt air in my lungs. And muscles like these!" He yanked up the sleeve of his cheap cotton shirt, one of the few pieces of clothing he had bought with his money. "Gold to buy real meat with."

"Humpf," his mother commented. "We'd starve first."

John London's tired voice broke in now. "Johnny's right, Flora," he said, risking her wrath as he had on a few occasions before. "That cannery's not right for a fine, husky fellow like our boy. He'd never get ahead there. We don't want to . . ."

His voice trailed off, but all four in that small, bare kitchen knew what he meant. *We don't want to drive him away again.*

Jack dropped his arms to his sides. He *had* looked for work. All day long he had walked the streets, stood in lines, heard doors slam before he even got inside. But everywhere he went a familiar whisper followed him, the same whisper that had followed him up and down the bay, across the ocean and back. *There is something more to life than this,* the whisper told him.

Eliza turned to the door, and Jack followed her outside. A full moon flooded the street. The smell of salt air drifted in from the bay, and he saw himself standing the night watch, filling his nostrils with the scent of tropical islands. But I don't want to go back, he told himself. "There's no future in it," he said aloud.

Eliza touched his arm. In the light of the moon he saw her plain, serious face as she turned to him.

"Don't worry, Jack. Take your time. You'll find something. I can help out a little longer."

Later when Jack slipped into bed in his little room, as usual he reached for one of the books that he had brought home from the library. A few hours of reading before sleep—that had been the pattern of his life since he had found the little Free Library beside the City Hall when he was ten years old. Even on the *Sophia Sutherland* he had read in his bunk by the light of a wick in a saucer of oil—read while his shipmates slept.

But tonight the words blurred on the page.

At last, with a deep sigh he turned out the light and lay staring into the dark. A good job—books—study.

That had been his plan. He had boasted about it all the way home from Yokohama. Since he was ten, he had always been able to find work—in a bowling alley—on an ice wagon—along the waterfront—in the cannery— on a sealing ship.

But now things were different. He was seventeen; he was a man. He had done a man's job for seven months and never once shirked. No child's job would do. Besides, in spite of the fact that he had never gone beyond grammar school, he knew that he wasn't like the rest of the boys who had grown up around him in West Oakland. They seemed content to go through life at a machine, doing the same dull, monotonous work from daylight to dark.

The trouble with me, he told himself at last, is that I opened the books. I know there's something more to life. But how can I find it?

It was a long time before he fell asleep. He still did not have the answer. But he knew that, for a while, he would have to take any job that he could get.

A whistle shrieked long and loud overhead. Another nearby joined in a higher key, announcing to the city of Oakland that the ten-hour work day in the mills and factories had ended. All around Jack, bobbin winders in the jute mill turned off their machines and shuffled toward the gates.

But Jack London's fingers did not hesitate. With quick,

deft movements he continued to thread the whirling, whining bobbins before him. It was child's work— stopping a bobbin with one hand, fastening a new thread with a quick loop of the weaver's knot, releasing the bobbin. Stopping another that had run out. Looping another knot.

For a month he had been going through these same monotonous motions, using none of the great muscles that he had developed on shipboard, tying thread in a lint-filled room instead of splicing thick rope on a foam-flecked deck, losing the heavy calluses on the palms of his hands but developing new ones on his flying fingers. And yet his muscles ached more at night than they had since he was fifteen.

The overseer passed behind him. "Overtime?" he asked.

"Yes, sir," Jack answered, taking some grim satisfaction in the knowledge that his fingers did not skip a motion. He was the best worker in the shed, he knew, and the manager had promised him a raise as soon as he had learned the ropes. He should have it any day now. A raise from a dollar a day to a dollar and a quarter. A dollar for his mother and a quarter for himself. Next year, if he stayed on, he might be an overseer. Some day a manager.

As he worked on, he tried to stifle his discontent by painting pictures in his mind of a bright future in the mill and a pleasant home in a nice district in Oakland. But the discontent remained.

At eight o'clock, Jack turned off his machine, and the wail of the whirling bobbins slowly subsided. Thirteen hours! The extra three hours made the difference between thirty cents in his pocket or nothing at all. By the time he walked home a mile and a half to save carfare and ate the supper that would be warming on the back of the stove, he knew he wouldn't be able to keep his eyes open long enough to read even the newspaper.

Outside the mill gate, a group of boys and girls stood whispering in the dark. As he walked east along the tree-shaded street, he passed girls strolling in pairs and felt their admiring glances. He tilted his cap at a rakish angle, but, under the glare of the street lamps at the corners, he could not bring himself to smile at any of them. His education on the waterfront and in the forecastle hadn't included instruction in how to meet girls from decent working-class families.

He jingled a few coins in his pocket. Maybe on Sunday I'll break loose, he thought. Go up to Blair Park and make a day of it!

But on second thought, he wasn't so sure. A fellow had to have a decent Sunday suit if he expected a girl to look at him twice. He had only his work clothes, and where was he going to get any others?

At 1321 Twenty-second Avenue, Jack slammed the front door and headed for the kitchen. He was ravenous, and the thought of food drove everything else from his head. He washed his hands at the sink, sloshed water over his face, and then sat down at the table.

Usually he helped himself to whatever he found on the stove and then read the newspaper while he ate in silence. But tonight Flora London flapped around the kitchen like a little bantam hen. She banged pans, opened and closed lids, and mumbled more to herself than to Jack.

" 'Fraid you'd be late tonight and the potatoes'd get mushy. Nothing worse than a mushy potato."

Jack looked up wearily, and to his astonishment saw her slap a large steak into the hot skillet. The aroma of sizzling meat filled the kitchen. He looked around, half expecting company to appear. But the steak was for him.

With a swoop, Flora descended upon him with the big coffee pot; a stream of hot amber liquid filled his cup to the brim and ran into his saucer. Back to the stove she flew, as though she must not lose a moment. She fished steaming potatoes from a kettle, plopped them onto a plate, and thrust it in front of him.

"Here, start on these. Know you must be starving. Steak's about done."

Silently Jack went to work on the potatoes and coffee. There was no doubt that his mother had something on her mind—something that concerned him, too. Maybe another of those get-rich-quick schemes that had kept them poor all their lives. In a few minutes she'd ask him for his overtime pay. But he wasn't going to be drawn into an argument until he'd finished that steak.

At last, when he could eat no more, he leaned back

in his chair and looked around for the newspaper. It was already past nine o'clock. In about eight hours his alarm would go off to start him toward another day at the mill. Now, if he could keep his eyes open a little longer, if his mother would let him alone. . . .

But Flora London, once she had taken hold of an idea, would not let it go. She swept the dishes from the table and slapped a copy of the San Francisco *Morning Call* before her son. It was carefully folded into a small rectangle.

"Thought you never would get home tonight, Jack. Read that! Just read it!" A small finger pointed to a column directly under his nose.

Jack read while his mother's voice went on.

"A twenty-five dollar prize, Jack. They've been having those writing contests every week, but this is the last one and the biggest. Just a few days left. You've *got* to try for it!"

Jack's tired eyes skimmed the announcement. "Amateur writing contest for young people . . . descriptive writing . . . word pictures . . . first prize, twenty-five dollars . . . second prize, fifteen dollars . . . third prize, ten dollars." So that was all that had been bothering her. His overtime pay was still safe.

He yawned, tucked the paper under his arm, and headed for the door.

"I'm tired, Ma. I couldn't write my own name. Been at the machine for thirteen hours. I'm going to bed."

23

But Flora's determined little body blocked the door. She threw the whole weight of her ninety pounds against his chest and pushed him back.

"Now you just listen to me, Jack London. You'd have to work in the mill for a month to earn that much money."

She snatched the paper from him and opened it to the front page. "Look at that headline. Just look at it. Every day this week, big stories on the front page about that wreck of the *City of San Francisco* at Point Bonita in the fog. What's so great about that? But everybody's talking about it."

Jack shrugged. "What's that got to do with me? I don't read that stuff. I've seen plenty of wrecked ships and sailed through fogs thicker than that one." He made another move toward the door.

"That's just it, Jack. You've seen a lot of things more exciting. All those stories you told us when you came home from sea. Just sit down and write one of them. It says here—'two thousand words.' Twenty-five dollars for only *two thousand words!*"

Slowly the fog in Jack's brain began to clear. The whine of spinning bobbins that seemed always in his ears became the whine of wind through the rigging of the *Sophia Sutherland.* Oh, he had stories to tell, all right. There was one—that typhoon off the coast of Japan. *That* would be a story for these landlubbers to read!

Flora, watching him, saw the change of expression

on his face. Quickly she swabbed the kitchen table with the tail of her apron and produced a tablet and pencil. Gently she pushed him toward the chair.

"Coffee's hot on the stove. Just take your time now. Nobody's going to bother you." She tiptoed out the door and closed it firmly behind her.

For a few minutes Jack stared at the lined paper while his thoughts flew back to a night that he could never forget. He heard again the call of the sailing master and the crash of the seas on the weather bow, felt the force of the storm stand up against him like a wall.

Slowly he picked up the pencil. Where to begin? Well, it really started in the morning, he decided, when the sun came up angry and red. A sailor's warning. His pencil touched the paper and he was off:

"It was four bells in the morning watch. We had just finished breakfast . . ."

The kitchen door creaked open. Jack heard his mother shuffle across the floor in her carpet slippers and shake the ashes in the stove.

"It's five o'clock. You'll have to stop now," she said as she emptied coffee grounds into the sink and ran fresh water into the pot. "I'll fix you a good breakfast. It's cold in here. You should have kept the fire going." She lifted the stove lid and stirred the ashes.

Jack yawned, stretched his cramped muscles, and stared at his mother with glazed eyes.

"Time is it?" he mumbled.

"Five o'clock, I said. Didn't think it would take you so long. Did you finish it?"

Jack shuffled through the pages on the table, slowly stacking them one by one into a neat pile.

"No. 'Bout half through, I guess."

"Half through? With all those pages? They said two thousand words, Jack. You wrote too much!"

"Yeh. Guess I did. But I'm not finished. It's hard to find the right words, Ma. Not like just telling about it to you folks." He staggered to the sink and rubbed cold water onto his numb cheeks and puffy eyes.

"But you can't stay home to finish. You'll be docked!" she wailed.

"Didn't say I'd stay home. I can finish tonight, maybe."

A pale glow was beginning to show in the east as Jack passed through the mill gate on this morning, but he did not notice it. And when he started home again the daylight was gone and he had not seen it. In his memory, however, was the strange soft light that had come off the ocean on the night of the big typhoon.

By the time he reached home, he was keyed to a high pitch, and as soon as supper was over he attacked his writing as though he had never left it. Sometime in the black of the night he staggered into his bedroom, set his alarm clock for five, and threw himself onto his bed fully clothed. He had finished!

The alarm wailed in the early morning, but he did

not stir. A few minutes later he felt himself being shaken violently.

"Get up, Jack. You'll be late," his mother's voice warned him.

Automatically he rolled out of bed and groped in the dark for his clothes until he found that they were still on him. He staggered out to the kitchen and blinked into the glare of the overhead light.

His mother stood at the table, the coffee pot in one hand and his stack of papers in the other.

"You wrote too much, Jack," she cried. "I warned you. Two thousand words. You've got four thousand. I counted them."

Jack slumped into the chair and gulped his bread, washing it down with steaming coffee. Slowly his mind began to stir.

"Guess I'll—I'll have to take out half of 'em," he mumbled.

Flora London's face crinkled into a deep frown of concentration as she cut another slice of bread from the loaf and laid it on Jack's plate. When she spoke again, her voice was softer.

"You're a good boy, Jack. Tomorrow's the last day— Saturday. You work on it tonight and copy it as nice as you can, and I'll take it over to San Francisco myself tomorrow morning. Now run, or you'll be late."

Friday night was like the others except that Flora sat in the kitchen with him, counting words, pouring coffee into his cup, and watching that he did not fall asleep. But at last he finished. Two thousand words, neatly copied. "The Story of a Typhoon off the Coast of Japan," by John London, Age 17.

Saturday, the separate bobbins blurred into one huge spinning mass and Jack's fingers fumbled for the loose ends that must be tied. But finally the day ended and he had his week's pay in his pocket.

Most of Sunday he slept, wakening only at his mother's insistence that he get up to eat. Late in the afternoon he went outside to sit on the steps and watch the sun go down. This was the day when he might have gone to Blair Park, he remembered vaguely.

At last, when his mind and body were rested for the first time in days, he began to wonder. That story. He couldn't even remember what he had written. Had he been the victim of just another of his mother's wild schemes? Or did she really think he could write a story that would win a prize?

Chapter **3**

On Monday evening when Jack London left the mill he hesitated at the gate for a few moments, sniffing the fresh night air and gazing up at the stars, automatically taking his bearings without aid of a compass. Within him stirred a vague unrest that seemed to turn his feet away from their usual homeward path.

For a month he had been going directly home each night, driven there not only by hunger and weariness, but by that plan that he had so determinedly made. Settle down, read, study—from the deck of the *Sophia Sutherland* on the homeward run, that had seemed to be just the life he wanted.

But now, as he turned reluctantly toward Twenty-second Avenue, toward the grim little house with its two elderly occupants who had become almost strangers to him over the years, he began to wonder.

I've roamed too much, he told himself. Roamed since I was a little kid hanging around the waterfront. The saloons and the waterfront vagrants seemed glamorous enough then, but they held no lure now. He had no desire to go back, but where could he go? Where but home?

As he swung along with his wide sailor walk, his mind turned back to school days. Old schoolmates—where were they? Once in a while on the streets he saw a face that he vaguely remembered. But he had been in so many schools—Garfield, Franklin, Cole—that he couldn't be sure. He had seldom played on the schoolgrounds after school with the other boys. He always had to work. Besides he had been shy, he remembered. Making friends wasn't easy for a country boy not used to town ways. He had got into the habit of doing things alone and keeping his nose in a book during recess and the lunch hour.

That was, until Frank Atherton moved to town from the country. Jack smiled to himself as he remembered that other shy awkward little fellow who followed him everywhere. They must have been about twelve years old, a couple of lone wolves until they found each other. For a while they did everything together, thought up one grand scheme after another. When he could steal the time from his various jobs, they tried to shoot ducks on the estuary with homemade slingshots and homemade bullets. He remembered a Saturday spent in hunting for wildcats in the hills back of Oakland. What a time they had had—clothes torn, faces and arms scratched from brambles, but not a wildcat to be found.

But then one day Frank moved away and he was alone again.

He was the only close friend I ever had, Jack told himself. Now, if Frank were here in Oakland, on a night like this we'd have a dozen plans to choose from. He shrugged his shoulders and tried to laugh off his depression. Guess I'm just lonesome, he decided.

The house was dark when he entered. A note on the kitchen table said that his parents had gone to Eliza's house. For a moment he thought of going, too, and then rejected the idea. They would talk and talk about his story, and he didn't want to think about it tonight. He didn't want to think about anything.

He raked lukewarm meat and potatoes from the skillet and gulped his food while he scanned the newspaper. Then he wandered into his bedroom.

The air in the little room was stale with smells that had drifted in from the kitchen. He stood with his legs apart as he had stood on many a watch at sea. His broad sailor shoulders seemed to fill the room and he spread his arms wide as though to push back the walls that were closing him in.

Suddenly he swung around, striking his heavy arm against the bedpost, and lunged toward the door, through the drab little parlor, and out into the night. He snatched his cap from his pocket, settled it onto the back of his head at an angle, and set off down the street. As though carrying out a plan that had lain dormant in his mind, that had never been expressed even to himself, he headed toward the little candy store on a side street a few blocks away. Around that store in the evenings, young people from the neighborhood lounged or strolled. This he knew. But he had never joined them.

As he drew near the street light at the corner, he slowed his pace, thrust his hands into his pockets, and whistled a little tune as he ambled along. He felt the coins in his pocket. He had been saving his money for a suit that he had seen in a secondhand store window. The price was ten dollars, and he wouldn't have that much for several more weeks. But if he went into the candy store he'd have to spend some of his money. He couldn't just walk in alone and stand around.

As he came closer to the lighted door, his feet dragged and a strange new sensation tingled his spine. He who had never known fear, who had sailed through the Bering Sea in fog and storm, who had rollicked over the bay, a daredevil who would never reef sail even in the stiffest wind—*he* was now afraid to walk into a candy store!

A few paces ahead of him strolled another lone boy who seemed vaguely familiar. Jack watched the way he walked with an easy, graceful stride, saw him tip his hat to two girls who were entering the store, heard him say, "Good evening," as he held the door open for them.

So that was the way it was done!

In the light from within, Jack recognized the good-

looking young fellow who conducted himself so gal-
lantly. He was the friendly apprentice in the blacksmith
shop down the street, a place he had wandered into a
number of times when he had been looking for work.
But tonight, with his hair slicked down, hat at a smart
angle, the apprentice looked different—like a real town
boy.

Jack followed him through the door. In the small
space between the glass cases and the wall, he tried to
remove his cap. But his arm refused to make the necessary graceful swing and he crammed his hands into his
pockets again. He walked slowly along the case, peer-
ing into it and scowling as though he were trying to make
a difficult decision, while he listened to the friendly
chatter behind him.

The girls seemed to know this other fellow. They
called him Louis. Should he turn around? Say "Hello"?
What if this Louis What's-his-name didn't recognize
him?

"Nickel's worth of red-hots," Jack finally blurted out
to the red-haired girl behind the candy case.

As soon as he had exchanged his nickel for the bag
of candy, there was nothing to do but turn around. He
sensed that the others were watching him, but he couldn't
be sure.

Clutching his candy, he forced himself to turn around
and face them.

"Hello, there," the boy named Louis said.

Jack's bronzed face broke into a broad smile revealing the wide space left by his two missing teeth.

Louis's face lit up at once. "I remember you. You were looking for a job. Did you find one?"

Jack nodded. "Yeh. Jute mill."

"Well—say—that's good. Nita," he called to the girl behind the counter. "I'll have red-hots, too. Say—this is— What's your name?"

"Jack. Jack London."

"This is Jack London. Friend of mine. Used to come into the shop regular."

This time Jack managed to pull his cap from his head as he acknowledged the introduction to Nita.

"Pleased to meet ya."

As Louis accepted his purchase he continued the introductions. His name was Louis Shattuck. The two girls with him were sisters. One was pretty, Jack saw at once. Her name was Mildred. The other wasn't much to look at.

By this time Louis was treating him like an old friend, and Jack glowed from the warmth of his geniality.

"The girls say they've got to get right home," he said. "Want to walk along?"

A new friend, and girls, too, all in a few minutes. This was more than Jack had imagined possible.

"Sure," he said, trying to sound casual.

Louis held the door and swept the others out with a wave of his hat. On the walk, he skillfully maneuvered to a place beside the pretty girl and started off down the street.

Jack followed with the plain little sister, wondering what to say to her, while he kept an admiring eye on Louis, who knew just what to do. When Louis opened his bag of red-hots and offered some to his girl, Jack followed his example. For quite a distance he managed to carry on a conversation about the merits of red-hots over some other forms of candy.

After the girls had been conducted to their doorstep and good nights had been whispered, Jack and Louis strolled back together.

"Is she—is that your girl?"

"Mildred? Oh, I take her out sometimes. No sense sticking to just one, though. It's more fun to have lots of 'em. You got a steady girl?"

Lots of 'em! Should he admit that he didn't have even one? But Jack knew he couldn't fool a fellow like Louis.

"No-o-o. You see—uh— I'm new around here. Been at sea for seven months and hunting a job and. . . ." He decided not to mention the reading and Sundays spent at the library.

"Well," Louis exclaimed, full of real sympathy for a fellow who didn't have a girl. "We'll have to get one for you. How about Mildred's sister?"

Jack hesitated and Louis laughed good-naturedly. "Not much of a looker, is she? Tell you what—tomorrow night we'll look around."

When they parted, they were old friends set upon a common goal. Jack *must* have a girl. Not to have one was unthinkable, and Louis Shattuck, Jack was convinced, was just the fellow to show him how to get one.

The next day at work Jack's thoughts were filled with girls. He watched those near him and heard them call back and forth to some of the fellows at other machines. But he also saw the scowls of the overseer and heard his sharp rebukes.

He decided against following their example; he wanted that raise to a dollar and a quarter. As soon as he got it he could quit each night when the whistle blew and have good long evenings with Louis Shattuck. Maybe he could find a good-looker like Mildred.

Jack stuck doggedly to his three hours of overtime. Then he dashed home, covering the distance in half the usual time. While his mother served his supper he scrubbed himself at the sink, worked a wet comb through his tangled mop of curly hair, and put on his other shirt. Louis, he noticed, had worn a different set of clothes in the evening—a suit, not new but not of the work variety —and he had definitely spruced up.

Flora London set the plate of food on the table with a loud "Hmpf!" But she had learned from experience that when Jack left home in the evenings she might as well not ask where he was going. He had never before paid much attention to his hair, however.

Each night that week, Jack met Louis Shattuck on

the street near the candy store, where they laid their
plans. Around here, an evening with a girl was simple,
Louis explained. You just went for a stroll or sat in
a park. In summer there were the band concerts to go
to, but those were over now. Sometime during the evening you had to buy something of course. Ice cream
or tamales, usually.

For a few nights, Louis asked one of his various girls
to bring along a friend for Jack, but each time she turned
out to be disappointing. Louis seemed to have picked for
himself all the choice girls in the neighborhood. Meanwhile Jack's money was disappearing rapidly and he
was getting nowhere.

Finally, on Friday night, Louis came up with another
plan. They would save their money for Sunday. They
would dress up, take the streetcar out through the hills
to Blair Park, and look around. If it was a nice day,
there would be plenty of girls out for the afternoon.

"You'll just have to pick out one for yourself," Louis
said. "Do what I do. Just walk along, tip your hat to a
good-looker, and get acquainted. All the fellows do it.
It's easy."

The idea sounded fine to Jack. He knew about Blair
Park—everybody in Oakland did. But he hadn't been
out there since he and Frank Atherton had explored it
when they were kids. He could still remember it, though
—the trails and nooks, the rustic bridges over a stream
that rushed through the deep canyon.

"Sure!" he agreed. "I was thinking about going out last Sunday."

It was not until the next morning that he began to worry. And then he worried all day. Louis had said they should dress up. That meant a suit and a hat. The girls wouldn't look at a fellow in his work clothes on Sunday.

On the way home from the mill with his week's pay in his pocket, Jack stopped in front of the secondhand store again. His pay and the money that he had been saving would buy that ten-dollar suit. There would be enough left over for one spree at Blair Park, but nothing for the rest of the week. And nothing for his mother. He could see her now, waiting at home for him as she waited every Saturday night.

The suit was still in the window. The price was still ten dollars. He leaned close to examine it through the dusty glass. It looked thin—a summer suit—and the cuffs were worn. But it was just about his size, he decided.

For several minutes he stood there, fingering the money in his pocket. And then he hunched his shoulders, turned away, and strode off toward home. I can't do it, he told himself. She's got to have the money for grub.

Late that night, as Jack tossed in his bed, he finally decided that there was only one thing for him to do. In the morning he'd have to go over to Eliza's and try to borrow one of his brother-in-law's suits. Captain Shepard was thirty years older than Eliza. He was almost an old man, tall and thin, and his clothes weren't the kind that any of the other fellows would be wearing, Jack knew. But there was no choice, now.

Maybe I won't even be able to get my arms into the sleeves, he told himself. But I'll have to try.

Only on Sundays did Jack waken in daylight. The jangle of the alarm clock, the plunge from deep warm sleep to the cold bare floor, the blind search for clothes in a black room—these things he accepted as a necessary part of the work day. On Sundays, however, he stayed in bed until his eyes opened of their own will. Sometimes it was the smell of coffee that brought him to pleasant consciousness. Or if the sun was high, the unaccustomed light gently nudged him awake. Usually he lay in bed for a few minutes, enjoying the luxury of idleness.

But on this Sunday morning, November the twelfth, he was startled from his sleep. Something was going on in the next room. The house shook, doors slammed, voices rose and fell. Neighbor children ran in and out. He heard Eliza's voice . . . Captain Shepard's . . . his mother's . . .

He leaped from bed, thrust his legs into his trousers, and dashed for the kitchen. It was full of people. In the center stood his father holding an armful of newspapers.

Before he could gasp a question, Eliza threw her arms around him.

"You did it! You won! *First* prize, Jack. *First* prize."

She thrust a newspaper under his nose. "Just look at that!"

His father was pounding his back as he tried to look. "Always knew you could do it, Johnny," he said. "All that reading you've been doing. I always said, 'Johnny's going to get somewhere, you just wait and see.'"

At last Jack made his way to a chair and spread the paper onto the kitchen table. At once the family, the neighbors, the children were silent as he read:

First prize, $25
Story of a Typhoon off the Coast of Japan
By John London Age 17
Address—1321 Twenty-second Avenue, Oakland

And there was his story, printed in the San Francisco *Morning Call*. His eyes skimmed through it from beginning to end.

"They changed some words," he said. "But it's all right. Gee! Twenty-five dollars! Why, that's—let's see —that's *two hundred and fifty hours* at the mill."

"I told you, Jack," his mother cried triumphantly. "I told you!"

Two hundred and fifty hours! His mind added and subtracted, multiplied and divided hours . . . days . . . words . . .

While the chatter went on around him he got slowly to his feet, thrust the paper into his pocket, and headed for the outdoors. He had to think. Twenty-five dollars!

As he wandered down the street, dazed by the incredible news, he kept going over what he had just read. That story was all right! There in the newspaper, all set up in print, it sounded good—like a real story in a book.

I've read a lot worse than that, he told himself.

And then, slowly a new idea began to take form. If he could write that one in three nights when he was working all day in the mill, what couldn't he do if he stayed at home and did nothing but write? Why, now that he had the hang of it, he could put out a story like that every day—or every other day, anyway. He began to multiply twenty-five dollars by thirty days, by three hundred, by . . .

"I'd be rich!" he cried aloud.

He laughed and struck out into a great stride, swinging his big shoulders as he dreamed great dreams. And me, worrying about a raise to a dollar and a quarter, he thought contemptuously. Worrying about a ten-dollar suit.

Suddenly he stopped short in the middle of the street. A suit. This was Sunday. He was going to Blair Park with Louis. But he didn't have a suit to wear! He yanked the paper from his pocket and stared at it. Twenty-five dollars, it said there, but he didn't have it yet.

And then he slapped the paper against his side and began to laugh. What am I worrying about? he asked himself. This paper's as good as money, any day, in a secondhand store.

His feet carried him at a run down an alley toward

the rear of that store, where the owner lived. As he slid to a stop and banged his fist against the door, he could already see himself decked out like the other fellows, spending his money freely on some pretty girl he was sure to meet in the park, making a date for the following Sunday afternoon.

But just as he heard the latch click from the inside, a sobering thought came to him. Maybe he shouldn't mention his story to Louis. He might not understand. There were some things that he had never talked about to Louis or any of the girls—things like going to the library on Sundays or reading every night in bed or sitting up for three nights to write a story because something besides his mother's urging had made him want to write it.

Chapter **4**

For another week, Jack's dreams of becoming a writer kept him at a high pitch. The screech of whirling bobbins, the thick lint-filled air that he breathed all day, the long monotonous hours were only temporary irritants now. The time when he would draw his week's pay and walk out of the mill forever was near.

The twenty-five dollar prize, promptly paid, had gone in a day: ten dollars to his mother, ten to the second-hand store, and five to redeem the watch that he had pawned soon after he returned from sea. But there was more where that came from, he was sure. Much more for things that paraded through his imagination—clothes, theater tickets, books, leisure in which to write and write.

Throughout his Sunday at Blair Park, a new feeling of power had carried Jack along, and he found to his surprise that he could match Louis Shattuck in attracting the best of the girls. His bulging biceps creased the sleeves of his new coat and his big shoulders strained the seams, but this evidence of manliness and strength, he found, made the girls turn to smile and linger near him. Why, it was no trick at all to get a girl. There was a little dark-eyed one who had promised to meet him at the bridge on the following Sunday. Oh, it had been a day, all right. But on the way home, he had decided that, like Louis, he wouldn't tie himself down to any one girl. There was no sense in sticking to just one when so many were available.

The feeling of power spread to the paper on which he wrote late at night. This second story of the sea gushed forth with all the extravagance of his new self-confidence. No two-thousand-word limit restrained him. No cutting out of precious words. In two evenings he finished it and confidently mailed it to the editor of the *Morning Call*. Maybe I'll get my pay before Saturday, he thought as later he swung along toward the candy store in search of Louis. Then I'll pick up my wages at the mill and quit for good. Just like that!

Each evening he hurried home to see if his check had arrived. On Saturday there was an envelope for him from San Francisco—a thick, bulky one. He ripped it open. Inside was his story and a small printed form saying that the *Call* would be unable to use the enclosed material. That was all. No letter. No explanation of why one story was worth twenty-five dollars and another was worth nothing at all.

For a moment anger rushed through him. He would go to San Francisco and demand an explanation! And then slowly the anger drained away.

He walked into his room, closed the door, and read again the first pages of his story.

"Gush," he said. "It's just gush."

He opened his bureau drawer and slid the envelope under the few things that he had brought home from sea —his oil skins—his so'wester—a rope mat that he had woven. And with that quick gesture he placed the story among things in his past that he had tried and had rejected. Along with it went the dreams for an immediate change in the pattern of his life.

Now it was more necessary than ever to escape from home in the evenings. But as the winter rains began and the nights turned colder, Jack and Louis were hard put to it to find amusement. Girls no longer strolled the streets; the candy store was cold and Nita stayed in a back room near the stove when there were no customers.

The two boys searched for places to go where they could be out of the cold. A Salvation Army tent meeting provided shelter, light, and people for a few nights. They tried saloons where, over a five-cent small beer, they could play two-handed euchre at a corner table. For several evenings they shivered in their summer suits in an old livery stable, playing their card games and wondering where to go next.

Gradually the life became intolerable to Jack. Where were his fine plans? He was getting nowhere. He could see a reflection of himself in all the discouraged, shabby men he passed on the streets—see himself growing older and shabbier, his fine muscles and splendid physique lost to the daily petty toil of the jute mill.

On a Saturday night in late winter, when again he found only the regular ten-cent pay in his envelope, he knew with sudden clarity that he had been a fool to hope for more. The promised raise would never come. Why should it when men, women, and children waited at the door every morning hoping for his job?

He walked through the gate and stood facing the west while the sharp, quick gusts of rain drenched him to the skin and set his teeth to chattering. From somewhere out of his past the old whisper came to him again, louder now than ever before, more insistent. *There must be something more to life than this,* it said.

With a sudden lurch, he turned away from the mill and swung off up the street.

"I'm never going back. Never!" he muttered.

By the time he reached home his spirit was almost joyful. He had put one more thing behind him. He was through with it as surely as he was through with other things that he had tried and rejected. But he had learned something. An unskilled man at a machine was nothing but a work-beast who would never get ahead.

What I need is a trade, he told himself. A trade with a future to it.

At home, Eliza was sitting in the kitchen with his father and mother. For once, he did not go to the sink to wash and prepare for an evening out, and his mother eyed him questioningly.

"Did you get your raise this week?" she asked as she slid the skillet to the front of the stove.

"No," Jack answered. "Never going to get it."

"What did they say, Jack?" Eliza asked.

"Nothing. Didn't say. I just know, that's all. I'm not going back."

Jack heard a spoon clatter as it hit the floor. He avoided his father's eyes.

"Not going back!" his mother cried. "What are you going to do? You're not going to sea?"

Jack shook his head. "No. I'm going to look around. I've got to have a trade—learn to do something special if I want to get ahead. That mill work—there's no future in it. Anybody can do what I've been doing. Even kids."

John London leaned forward, rested his arms on the table, and stared at his knotted, idle hands. And then he raised his eyes to the strong, healthy boy across from him.

"You're right, Johnny," he said. "Learn to do something with your hands that you can be proud of. You remember when I had a farm, I grew the best tomatoes and corn of anybody around. I was proud of them. On a farm there's always plenty to eat and no overseers. I always thought—if you could get a little piece of land somehow, I could help. . . ."

47

"No!" Jack exploded. "I hated the farms."

But when he saw the hope drain from his father's face he softened his voice. "No, Pa. I couldn't be a farmer. I'm used to the city now. Anyway, farmers are having a bad time these days. No, I want to find something that's new—maybe something that I can study and read about."

His mother put his supper before him and then sat down at the table with the others. Out of the corner of his eye, Jack saw the little frown between her eyes, but she wasn't going to fight him this time, he noted. Not yet, anyway.

He glanced at Eliza. Maybe she'd offer to help out again while he had a chance to look around. But she was concentrating on an idea, her angular face intense with the desire to solve another problem for her brother.

"I've been thinking . . ." she said quietly. "You want something new. Well, I've been reading in the papers that they're going to put in more electric street lights. And the street railways—why, it was just a few years ago when the cars were all horse-drawn. Maybe you could learn about electricity."

Electricity! Why hadn't he thought of it? Now *there* was a *big* idea.

Jack banged his fist on the table. "That's it!" he exclaimed. "Just the ticket. They've got to have more electricians around here, and where'll they get 'em?"

"But how're you going to learn?" his mother asked. "Trade schools cost money!"

Jack thought for a moment. In many of the stories that he had read when he was young, the poor boy got ahead by hard work and perseverance. He started at the bottom, worked up, and in time he was the manager and married the owner's daughter. Some of those boys he had read about weren't as strong and healthy as he was, either.

"I'll start at the bottom," he announced. "I'll watch and listen and read up at night. I can get books at the library and surprise 'em with what I know. They're going to add some new lines to the street railway. Why, I'll bet they need more men right now. First thing Monday morning I'll go out to the power plant and tell 'em what I've got in mind."

Jack was first at the gate to the power plant on Monday morning. It was only three miles from home out on San Leandro Road, and he could have walked; but he had decided to ride the street car to watch just how things were done. He sat directly behind the conductor, and by the time he reached his destination he felt satisfied that he knew a great deal about the operation of the cars. There was nothing to it.

As soon as the doors were open he made his way directly to the superintendent's office. No sense in talking to anyone else. He had made up his mind, during his Sunday at the library, that this time he would leave no doubt about his intentions. He was not interested in just getting a job. He wanted to learn the whole business,

from bottom to top, and he would make this clear from
the start.

As Jack walked down the freshly painted corridor
of the office section of the plant, resplendent under
electric lights, he smiled. This is the place for me, he
thought. Sure different from the dumps I've worked in.
At the door lettered in black, SUPERINTENDENT: MR.
GRIMM, he paused, tucked his clean shirt more firmly
into his trousers, slipped his cap into his pocket, and
ran his fingers through his hair. Then he knocked.

"Come in," a deep voice barked.

He pushed open the door and stood for a moment on
the threshold while his eyes took in the splendid room
—comfortable chairs, books, carpet, polished desk. He
had never seen anything so fine! And behind the desk sat
a man who *looked* like a superintendent. He was tall and
dignified, with a crest of silvery hair and bushy side
whiskers.

"Good morning, sir," Jack said, pleased that his voice
did not falter.

Superintendent Grimm's eyes took in the powerful
arms and shoulders and the sturdy legs of his early
morning visitor. And then the scowl that had marked
his face gradually changed to a faint smile. His voice
took on a pleasant tone.

"Well, come in. Come in, young man. What do you
want? A job?" He motioned to a chair.

Jack lurched toward the chair, regretting his rolling

gait that made every room seem too small for him. He sat down and clutched the arms before he answered. The sentences that he had been formulating since his decision on Saturday night came forth automatically.

"I've come to see you, sir, because I want to become an electrician. I've given it a lot of thought, and I've decided that I want to devote my life to this work."

There! He had said it, and it sounded fine.

The superintendent stared at him, and then he shifted in his chair and cleared his throat.

"You look like a bright young man," he said. "What is your name?"

"London. Jack London."

"Do you know anything about electricity?"

"I've been reading up," Jack answered, trying to convey the impression that this had been a lifelong ambition. Indeed, at the moment, he was sure that he had never wanted to do anything else.

"I'm used to hard work," he went on, rubbing a hand along the muscles of his arm. "You can see I'm strong and healthy. What I want to do is start at the bottom and work up, learn all there is to know about electricity, and spend my whole life at this work."

He leaned back, satisfied. He had put his cards right on the table, just as he had made up his mind to.

Superintendent Grimm's face broke into a wide, benevolent smile. He leaned across the desk and looked Jack straight in the eye.

"Well, now, that's the way I like to hear a young man talk," he said. "Too many of our young people these days never look ahead. All they want is a soft job. But there's no limit to a career in electricity for an ambitious young man who is willing to work hard. I know. I started at the bottom."

As the superintendent leaned back in his chair and began to explain in detail the different divisions of work in the power plant, Jack's thoughts soared through the years ahead of him. Up and up he would climb until he, too, had an office like this where he would interview other young men and tell them of his own climb to the top.

"Of course, before you can get into the more complex operations, you will want to work in the car house where the machines are installed. All the electricians there started as helpers, sweeping up, washing windows, and so forth. Before that, naturally, they worked as oilers in the engine room. You have no idea how complicated the steam engines are.

"Everything there depends upon the fire room," he went on, expanding upon the intricacies of this great plant, beaming on Jack all the while. "People don't realize that we must weigh every pound of coal we burn to determine which firemen are able to get the most out of the coal they shovel into the furnaces. Why, coal is the very basis of this great industry."

He got up from his chair, walked around the desk, and

laid a fatherly hand on Jack's shoulder. "Well, Jack," he said, "when would you like to start?"

"Any time," Jack answered, too dazed by his good fortune to comprehend that he was hired and already on his way.

"Very well. You can begin tomorrow morning at seven o'clock. Come, I'll show you around." He waved Jack through the door.

From one part of the plant to another they walked while Jack's head buzzed with new words, figures, statistics. Every man they passed was hard at work keeping the great street railway moving. Over the din in the steam engine room he caught only a part of the explanation, but he was awed by the great engines and the skill of the men who operated them.

At last they came to the fire room where workers, stripped to the waist, fed huge shovelfuls of coal into the gleaming open mouths of the great furnaces. The air was stifling, and Jack saw perspiration stream down the backs of the firemen.

The superintendent took him to an anteroom where a huge stack of coal had been deposited.

"You will start as a coal-passer," he explained. "You fill the wheelbarrow and take it over there to the scales where you weigh it before you dump it on the plates in front of the furnaces. You can imagine what would happen if one of the men would run out of coal. The whole system would break down."

And then he added, almost as an afterthought, "When the day firemen are supplied, stack the coal for the night firemen against the wall, weighing it, of course, to be sure you have the same amount. That's all."

Back in the office Jack learned the rest of the story. His salary would be thirty dollars a month for ten-hour days, including Sundays and holidays. He would have one day off each month. But before the superintendent sent him on his way he gave him a small bonus—a streetcar pass.

"Use it whenever you want to," he said, patting Jack on the shoulder again, "and sit wherever you like. Unless, of course, a paying customer needs a seat. Then you'll want to stand."

Jack was outside the plant before he fully comprehended all that he had been told. He had a job, all right. A man-sized job. No women or children could do this work! But his mind protested. Only thirty dollars a month. Why, I was making that in the cannery when I was a kid, he thought. And now I'm a man, still working at a boy's wages.

He swung onto a streetcar, showed his pass, and slumped down in a seat. Until a cold breeze hit his back, he had not realized that his shirt was damp with perspiration.

"Whew," he muttered. "Coal-passer at thirty dollars a month. Not even Sunday off."

All the way home he wrestled with the problem. Why

couldn't he, a strong, healthy fellow, earn more than that? He turned the question over and over in his mind, and by the time he reached his corner he believed that he had the answer. Always before, he had been an unskilled worker. Now he was beginning to work up toward a career. Surely from now on things would be different.

The next morning, dinner pail in hand, he climbed onto the six-fifteen car, eager to start the day. Tonight I'll have to see Louis and explain about Sundays, he reminded himself. But I won't be on this job long. I'll move up as soon as Mr. Grimm sees what a worker he's hired.

In the coal room he stripped to the waist and went to work at top speed, determined to be best coal-passer the superintendent had ever hired. He slashed into the coal heap, filled his iron wheelbarrow, carted it to the scales, and dumped his load. Back he rushed to repeat the process, throwing all of his strength into the task. By ten o'clock he was shaking with exhaustion and hunger.

Quickly he reached into his dinner pail for two slices of bread and butter, wolfed them in seconds, and continued with his labor. Soon afterward he reached into the pail again until, by eleven o'clock, his lunch was gone. Lunch hour came and he worked on. When the whistle blew at six, the day firemen left and the night firemen came on. Still the required amount of coal had not been passed.

At eight-thirty, his knees buckling under him, he dumped the last load, painfully washed the grime from his hands and face, and pulled on his shirt. He tottered out to the streetcar and sank down in a corner seat. His head fell forward and he sat in a stupor of exhaustion as the car moved toward the center of Oakland.

Gradually the car began to fill up until, about halfway home, Jack became aware that a woman had got on for whom there was no seat. Dully he remembered the conditions of his pass and struggled to rise. But he could not move. In the cold wind that blew through the car his muscles had stiffened. He grasped the edge of the seat and tried again, but he could not budge. The car drew nearer and nearer his corner while he worked first one cramped leg and then the other. Someone pushed him to his feet and he hobbled into the aisle and toward the door.

At his corner he staggered to the ground and limped the two blocks home.

The kitchen was a blur of smells and light and voices. He fell into a chair, reached for bread, and crammed it into his mouth. His head dropped onto the table and he felt his mother shake him, heard her cry, "John! John!"

Then his father's voice joined hers. "What happened to you, Johnny? Johnny!"

The last things he felt that night were his parents' hands as they dragged him to his room, pulled his clothes from him, and covered him.

In the early morning he wakened in an agony of pain. His hands and wrists were on fire, rigid with swelling. He could not close his fingers or even pick up his clothes. But somehow, with the help of both his parents, he got to the table and consumed a huge breakfast.

"Got to have more lunch, Ma," he insisted. "Wasn't half enough."

At last he clamped his stiff fingers around the dinner pail and hobbled to the streetcar.

The second day was worse than the first. Each shovelful of coal was agony for his sprained wrists. At times he sank down in the privacy of the coal room and wept in rage and despair. But he went on. Before noon one of the day firemen, a big-muscled, kind-faced man who had been watching him, took pity on him.

"Come here, boy," he whispered.

He produced two wide leather straps and bound them tightly around Jack's swollen wrists.

"That'll help," he said. "Used to wear 'em all the time, myself."

Again that night, Jack was helped to bed. As in a nightmare, he limped to work on the following morning. Day after day he continued, dreaming only of his time off at the end of the month when he could sleep and sleep for a whole day. There were no hours of reading. No evenings with Louis. No girls. No sunny days at Blair Park. Spring! He scarcely saw the sun.

Finally, one morning, the kindly day fireman stopped him and looked around carefully before he spoke.

"I'm goin' to tell you something," he whispered, "but I'll lose my job if anybody finds out. You've got to promise you won't tell on me."

"Sure," Jack answered, leaning on his shovel and mopping the blackened perspiration from his face and neck.

"I'd have let you know sooner, only I thought you'd quit after a few days. You're doin' the work of two men. Used to be a day coal-passer and a night coal-passer, and each of 'em got forty dollars. They quit because they weren't makin' enough for the work they were doin'."

He turned away quickly and threw another shovelful of coal into the furnace. "Now, don't tell on me," he pleaded. "Superintendent said he'd fire any of us that told you."

Two men! Slowly Jack pushed his empty wheelbarrow to the coal pile while his thoughts moved back to that morning in the superintendent's office. He saw the gleaming desk, the imposing white hair and whiskers, the benevolent smile. He heard the glowing promises of a career in the business and remembered his surprise at getting such a fine job so quickly.

"So that's why!" he muttered. "Two men. That's eighty dollars. Talked a dumb kid like me into saving him fifty dollars a month!"

He threw the shovel onto the floor as rage burned through him. And then slowly he picked it up again, filled the wheelbarrow, and pushed it to the furnace.

"You quittin'?" the fireman whispered.

"No," Jack answered, his lips tense. "Not 'til I show him that I can get all the coal in by six o'clock. Then he'll see what kind of a worker he's lost!"

The day finally came when Jack dumped his last load just as the six o'clock whistle blew. He said good-by to his friend, the fireman, but there was no triumph in his voice. In what had become an almost permanent condition of exhaustion, he wanted only one thing—to get home and into bed. Then he would sleep and sleep. He didn't care if he never got up again.

Chapter **5**

On a green-painted bench of the small triangular City Hall Park in the center of Oakland, Jack London sat in warm early-April sunshine, his head bent over a book. Beside him on the bench lay other books that he had borrowed from the Free Library next door to the City Hall. People moved along the paths and lingered near the bandstand, but he did not notice them.

He was reading, for the second time, Herman Melville's *Typee*. He had first read it before he went to sea; but now, with the smell of tropical islands still in his memory, he found new pleasure in it. The Marquesas of the story were farther south than the *Sophia Sutherland* had gone, he knew. He had not seen them. But some day I will, he promised himself. Some day I'll sail all over the world!

He dropped the book into his lap and stared out over the small triangle of grass that covered the little park. In

spite of all the books that he was able to read now, and
the warm sun that he could sit in every day, he was restless. After he had quit his job in March and had slept
until he could sleep no more, he had wandered from one
end of Oakland to another, standing for hours on the
waterfront, listening to the idle talk of idle men, and
thinking . . . thinking . . .

He looked down at his small wrists, still bound by
leather straps. He examined his hands. Embedded under
his nails and in the creases of his knuckles were fine
particles of coal that would not wash away. The sight
of his hands and wrists filled him with disgust. Work! The
thought of it sickened him.

Every day his mother's tight lips reminded him that
he must find something to do, and soon. He knew that
he could probably get another job in a mill or factory if
anyone could, but it would be the same story. Ten cents
an hour. Ten hours and more a day. Nothing to look
forward to. Nothing to look back on. He'd be just another piece of machinery until his muscles gave out.
Then he'd be dumped onto the scrap heap with the other
forlorn men who lined the streets.

While Jack sat on the bench bitterly reviewing his
problem, a new and strange noise began to stir the air. To
his ears came the roll of drums, the shrill piping of a fife,
the heavy tramp of feet.

At once a crowd rushed into the little park; men and
boys climbed to the bandstand for a better view. An

excited boy jumped onto the bench beside Jack and shouted over the heads of the people.

"It's the army! They're marching on City Hall! There's Colonel Baker on his horse!"

Jack gathered up his books and stepped onto the bench. His eyes followed the pointing finger of the boy beside him.

Rounding the corner of Broadway was a magnificent white horse mounted by a tall, imposing man wearing a huge sombrero. Behind him swarmed a mass of followers. But this was no army in uniform. It was a great crowd of tattered men like those who lined the waterfront, slept in the parks, and stood all day outside employment offices. Jack could already make out the words on the banners they carried:

INDUSTRIAL ARMY   ON TO WASHINGTON
GIVE US TRANSPORTATION.

As the mob drew close to the steps of the City Hall, well-dressed men and women fell back but Jack held his place. Everywhere he had been hearing about these men. He knew that groups of the desperate, hungry unemployed were organizing all over the country in this depression year of 1894. Their voices were growing louder and louder as they demanded help from their government.

In Ohio, a group called the Commonweal of Christ, under the leadership of a man named Coxey, had already set out for Washington to demand that Congress pass a "good-roads" bill and put the unemployed to work building public roads. Six hundred men had also left Los Angeles in March. And now, here in Oakland, was another great army preparing to cross the country.

Jack forgot his books, his dreams of tropical islands. Caught up in the excitement, he watched and listened.

Suddenly, out of nowhere, uniformed police appeared and slashed through the crowds. But the horde of hungry, determined men came on. At the City Hall a young man leaped up the steps and raised his arms.

"That's Kelley! General Kelley!" someone shouted.

Jack, defending his place on the bench, heard the "General" begin to speak. Through the clamor around him he listened and learned. The railroads were denying the Industrial Army free transportation. Citizens were raising money to ship them out in box cars, but the men demanded better treatment. They were not hogs!

At last the police managed to break up the mob, but rumbling groups of men walked the streets all day talking, arguing, persuading. Jack followed on the outskirts, listening. His reason told him that the problems stifling his country could not be solved by a few thousand men marching on Washington. A good-roads bill would not take care of the children in the jute mill and cannery, or of people like Mr. Grimm.

Yet the idea became more and more exciting. He went down to the encampment on the mud flats of the estuary and, wandering from one group to another, heard of the plan to take over Mill's Tabernacle on Eleventh and Harrison Streets that night. Somewhere along the way he made up his mind. There was nothing to hold him here in Oakland, and the march to Washington promised the fun that he had had so little of—fun, and a chance to see the country.

It was supper time before he got what he was waiting for—the whispered word that the "army" would leave at seven in the morning. Then he set out at a run for home. There he raced up the steps and through the door.

"I'm going to Washington!" he cried to his startled parents as he threw himself into a chair and began to devour bread and butter.

"Stop stuffing yourself, Jack," his mother complained. "If you'd come home for dinner instead of chasing around all day, you wouldn't be so starved by supper time. What's that you said about Washington?"

"I'm going to Washington, D.C., with Kelley's Army. Leave at seven in the morning." There wasn't time to explain. He had things to do: take books back to the library . . . get a coat somehow . . . say good-by to Eliza. . . .

John London stroked his gray beard while he kept an eye on his wife. "It's been in the papers all week, Flora," he said quietly. "Big crowd going off to Washington to get something done about unemployment. Maybe Johnny can help."

"Help!" Flora's fierce little eyes seemed to pierce the thick lenses. "And what about us? What're *we* going to do?" she wailed.

Between bites, Jack tried to placate her. "I won't be gone long, Ma," he said. "We're taking the train out in the morning and we'll be in Washington in no time at all. After we get things squared up there, I'll be back. Then I'll—I'll—"

He dashed out the door and sprinted the few blocks to Eliza's house. She would help. She always did. And she would understand the vague, unformed whispers that urged him to go off adventuring again before he tried to settle down once more.

At five-thirty the next morning, when his alarm went off, Jack jumped out of bed and threw on his clothes, worn flannel shirt and trousers and an old overcoat that Eliza had contributed. Though it was spring in Oakland, it would be cold in the mountains. He crammed a book into each overcoat pocket and slipped into a trouser pocket a small notebook and pencil and the two five-dollar gold pieces that Eliza had given him. He was ready to go.

Cap in hand, he ventured into the kitchen. In stony silence his mother was cooking breakfast. He noticed that she was preparing twice the usual amount, and for a moment he felt a twinge of guilt.

"I won't be gone long, Ma," he said. "When we get

things settled in Washington there ought to be good jobs for everybody."

John London came into the kitchen just as Jack rose to leave. He put his arm across the boy's broad shoulders. His voice trembled as he spoke. "Take care of yourself, Johnny," he said. "Don't get into trouble there in Washington. That's a long way from home and we can't. . . ."

"You're all we've got, Jack!" his mother cried as he went through the door.

He looked back once and waved good-by to the two elderly people standing forlornly in the doorway. And then he raced toward Mill's Tabernacle nearly two miles away.

After the first mile he slowed down a bit. He was early. It was only a little after six o'clock on this Friday morning, April 6, 1894. The sun was barely peeking over the hills to the east. In the west a great bank of fog hung over the ocean. Only yesterday he had believed that he almost hated Oakland. But today, now that he was leaving, he knew that it was only the uncertainty of his life that he hated.

Probably before he got back from this new adventure, his mother would have moved to another house. But it wouldn't matter. He had no fondness for any house; he had lived in too many.

By the time he returned, surely he would have some plan for his future. Meanwhile, adventure lay before him. The other men in Kelley's Army might be going on this trip for the cause. But he still knew in his heart that he was going only for adventure and fun and a chance to see the country.

As he drew near Mill's Tabernacle, he listened for the noise of men preparing to depart. But the city was unusually quiet. Uneasy, he sprinted the last few blocks. Around the open door of the tabernacle stood a small group of men.

"Where are they?" he cried as he skidded to a stop.

"Gone," a forlorn voice answered. "Police routed 'em out at two o'clock and packed 'em into boxcars at the Sixteenth Street Station. Must be in Sacramento by now."

"Cleaned 'em out and left a whole bunch of us behind," another grumbled.

Jack glanced wildly around. From all directions men were straggling up. At the corner, four policemen armed with guns and clubs stood ready for trouble. But the leaderless, dejected group made no move.

Without a word, Jack dashed in the direction of the station. Gone! Left behind!

The station was empty except for a few stragglers and a battalion of police and firemen who eyed him suspiciously. He wandered out along the track and kicked some lumps of coal into the bushes. An empty boxcar attracted him until a policeman came up from behind and tapped him on the shoulder.

"Move on," he commanded.

Jack moved. He wasn't a bum. He had ten dollars in

his pocket and as much right as anyone to look into a boxcar, he told himself. But the guardians of the law and the railroads were in an ugly mood this morning.

He jingled the two gold coins in his pocket, and then, suddenly, he made up his mind. The army would camp in Sacramento tonight. He'd buy a ticket and join them there. Let the other fellows hang around Oakland! He was going to Washington with Kelley's Industrial Army, and who could stop him?

For ten days Jack endeavored to catch up with the army by any means that he could find, but always they remained ahead of him, hurried on from town to town by local authorities. He bought no more tickets, but he rode the railroads, nonetheless, in boxcars, on top of mail cars, on the rods beneath four-wheel passenger cars. Soon he acquired an entirely new language—the language of the tramp and the road. In a few days he was so proficient with his new words that they came naturally to his lips.

As a tramp, or "stiff," his wants were simple. He needed food. For this he "threw his feet" to back doors in the towns for a "handout" or a "setdown." Or he begged on the streets, the "main stem," for a "light piece." From hardened road tramps, the "blowed-in-the-glass profesh," he learned to "hold down" a train despite every effort of the brakemen, the "shacks," to "ditch" him. He learned to race alongside a fast-moving train and jump onto the platform, the "blind" of a "blind baggage"—a car with no door at the end—where he would be safe from the "shacks" until the train stopped. In towns, the police were "bulls" to be avoided at all cost.

In spite of the constant risks, the cold of the mountains, the scorching sun of the desert, flying cinders, and hunger, he enjoyed every moment of his new freedom. Sometimes he was alone, sometimes in the company of other stiffs. But the chief difference between him and the men he met on the road was the fact that in his pockets he always carried books bought for a few cents in secondhand stores along the way. Waiting beside the tracks for the next train or lying on the floor of an empty boxcar, a "side-door Pullman," he read.

Ten days after he left sunny Oakland, Jack was sidetracked in an open blind at the summit of the mountains beyond Laramie, Wyoming. A fierce blizzard was raging and he was in agony. A few days before, a flying redhot cinder had burned a path down the back of his overcoat where the bitter wind and snow now found their way.

He was in trouble, serious trouble, he knew. A man could freeze in no time in weather like this. But where could he go? What should he do? Should he climb down, make for the cab, and try to talk the fireman into letting him shovel coal? It was a slim chance, but just when he had decided to risk it, a brakeman came by and flashed his lantern through the swirling snow. He was caught!

"Hey, you," he said. "Ain't you froze yet?"

"Nope," Jack replied through chattering teeth.

"Well, come on down."

Jack climbed down and stood shivering in the snow while the shack looked him over.

"You're a sight. Tryin' to kill yourself?" He waved his lantern off across the tracks, and then his voice took on a kinder tone. "There's a refrigerator car full of guys over there . . . say they're tryin' to catch up with Kelley's Army. Ought to be room for one more."

Jack squinted suspiciously through the whirling snow and sighted the outline of a refrigerator car. Maybe this is a trick, he thought. But I couldn't be worse off.

"Thanks," he said and stumbled across the tracks.

The door to the car was open, and Jack peered cautiously in. He could see nothing in the blackness. He climbed up and stepped inside. Something soft gave under his foot.

"Git off my leg," a voice howled.

"Ouch! My arm! What the . . ."

He stumbled forward, and a mass of arms and legs hurtled him on. Each time he fell he struck an arm, a leg, a head. And each time he was tossed forward. Down the length of the car and back he went until at last he dropped on a straw-covered spot where he lay panting and bruised.

At once a laugh started beside him that rang down

70

the length of the car. And then suddenly he began to laugh, too. The joke was on him; he had been initiated.

"How many men in here?" he finally gasped.

"Eighty-four. You make eighty-five. You're a member of the Nevada Push now."

All the way across the mountains and down through Western Nebraska the fun continued. Every man had to tell a story, and if it wasn't better than the one before it, he was put through the "threshing machine" that Jack had experienced. The heat of eighty-five bodies on top of a layer of straw kept them warm.

But when twenty-four hours had passed and the men had eaten nothing, they decided upon a course of action. They took up a collection and at the next stop wired ahead to Grand Island that eighty-five hungry men would arrive at noon and must be fed.

As they rolled through Nebraska the warm spring sun came out and citizens of Grand Island waiting along the tracks were hailed by eighty-five ragged men dangling their feet from tops of freight cars. Police held the train at the station, escorted the men to hotels and restaurants where they consumed enormous meals, and escorted them back again to the station.

In great spirits, the Nevada Push rolled on toward Omaha. But there, suddenly the holiday atmosphere changed. At one o'clock in the morning, in a downpour, Jack and his eighty-four companions were met by the militia and hustled across the Missouri River bridge to

Council Bluffs, Iowa. Five miles away, in Chautauqua Park, they were told, Kelley and his followers were encamped. The police lined up to escort them out of town.

Jack pulled his cap down over his ears and felt the river of water course down his back. Five miles through the dark and pouring rain!

"Not me," he muttered to a companion called The Swede. "I'm going to hole up somewhere until daylight."

"Me, too!" The Swede agreed.

They watched their chance and slipped off into the dark.

The Swede was shivering. "Where'll we go?" he whispered, fumbling for Jack's coattail in the dark.

"There ought to be some place that's warm around here," Jack mumbled as he pushed ahead, hands extended in front of him.

He felt his way around the corner of a building that seemed to be on stilts. He tried the doors and windows.

"Come on, Swede," he called. "We've got to break in."

They threw their weight against the door and crashed inside. The Swede produced a match from an inside pocket, and in the faint sputtering light they glanced quickly around.

"It's a saloon!" Jack cried. But when he saw the empty shelves and felt the wind blowing up through holes in the floor he understood. "Empty," he wailed. "They're moving her someplace."

The Swede's match went out, but Jack could hear him beating his arms against his sides.

"I'm froze!" he moaned.

Jack crawled up on top the bar, shivering in his wet clothes. The Swede curled up on a table. There they shook and groaned through the long hours until dawn.

At five o'clock they could stand no more. Jack poked his head out the door and through a mist saw railroad tracks. "Too many bulls around this burg for me," he said. "I'm going to hop a freight back to Omaha and throw my feet for grub. Then I'll head for camp. You coming?"

His miserable companion shook his head. "No," he moaned. "I'm goin' to head out fer Chicago and get me a job. No more hoboin' fer me."

It was ten-thirty when Jack finally reached camp. Through driving rain he sighted the bedraggled army, grown now to about sixteen hundred men, standing in a pall of smoke from feeble campfires, soaked to the skin, tattered, hungry. The big, dry amphitheater was filled with militiamen.

Jack soon found his group. Overnight it had become Company L of the Second Division. From all sides he heard the news. No more rides on the railroads. The Pinkertons, railroad detectives, were manning every car. Not even a "blowed-in-the-glass profesh" could hold down a train across Iowa now.

With good humor, Jack entered into the spirit of the company as they slogged seven miles through mud and rain to the little town of Weston. Here two railroads met, and it was the plan of the leaders to capture a train by force of numbers and load the army onto it.

All the next day, the men lay beside the tracks, waiting, bragging of how they would swing up onto the platforms when the train slowed for the station. No more boxcars for them! They would ride in style to Washington.

The lines were unusually quiet that day. Not a train came through for hours. And then from the west the whistle of a locomotive brought everyone to his feet. Jack took his place close to the track, testing the gravel beneath his feet, every nerve ready for the quick leap.

Suddenly a train thundered through the town at top speed, scattering dirt and cinders into the astonished faces of the waiting mob. In a moment another came screeching by, its whistles hooting in derision. Then another. Train after train dashed through the town of Weston that day carrying every kind of car—mail cars, flat cars, cabooses, old worn-out rolling stock.

"They've cleaned 'em out!" someone shouted. "Cleaned out Omaha and Council Bluffs. Every last car gone east!"

For two days the men hung around Weston while their clothes dried out in the pale sun. Sympathetic citizens from as far away as Omaha sent supplies and wagons. Finally, there was nothing to do but walk. Headed by Kelley on a black horse, flags and banners bravely flying, to the beat of fife and drums the sixteen hundred men set out for Des Moines, one hundred and forty miles away.

The "Nevada Push," Company L of the Second Division, brought up the rear, and Jack straggled along at the rear of his company. As the sun dried the dirt of the road, a great cloud of dust from the hundreds of feet drifted over the rolling land to announce their coming. When the road curved, Jack could see ahead the whole length of the incredible procession: first Kelley, riding comfortably along; then the commissary wagons on which some of the more fortunate also rode.

Until the realization slowly came to him that he was actually going to be forced to walk one hundred and forty miles across the farm lands of Iowa, Jack willingly put up with the hardships. But this he hadn't bargained on. He had come along for adventure and fun and a chance to see the country. He was seeing the country, all right. And more adventure might be ahead.

But fun! It was no fun to tramp hour after hour along a road in worn-out shoes for a cause that he was not much concerned with. At this rate they would be months getting to Washington.

By the end of the first day, the sole of Jack's left shoe was flapping ominously. On the second day, both soles came off and he walked in his socks. Not until he tramped in bare feet did the commissary produce another pair of "kicks" for him, but by that time his feet were so bruised and swollen that the new shoes made blisters. Each night he counted his blisters and in his small note-book-diary he wrote about the condition of his feet.

For the people of Iowa, however, the march of Kelley's Industrial Army was a great event. Entire communities turned out as though the circus had come to town. Women brought hot lunches to the roadside for the marchers, and at night families wandered through the camps, listening to the political speeches and the singing. In the mornings, men brought wagons to help transport some of the baggage, and Jack soon managed to get rides by one means or another, while his blisters healed.

But after ten days, when they finally straggled into Des Moines, all of the men were so footsore that they declared they would walk no more. They took over the old stove works near the railroad tracks, and refused to budge.

For Jack, this was fine. Washington could wait. The weather was cold but clear, Des Moines was providing food, and all day he could watch baseball games between the Des Moines Stars and the army team. At night he slipped past the pickets into the city for a "light-piece" with which to buy books or other necessities. Since the commissary was low on clothing, he used his talents at "throwing his feet" to the doors of the best houses in town and always came back with his arms loaded.

For Des Moines, however, the situation was intolerable. Even the most sympathetic citizens knew that they could not go on providing three meals a day for sixteen hundred men, and still the railroads refused to transport them.

At last someone had an idea. They would build tenfoot flatboats in which the men could float down the shallow Des Moines River to the Mississippi and then on to the Ohio River on which they could float as far as West Virginia.

Boats! This was something Jack knew about. He was Sailor Jack again as he helped with the building and caulking of one hundred and thirty-four boats in three days. The one he chose for himself he christened *The Pirate*. He picked nine hustlers for his crew: Scotty, Davy, McAvoy, Fish, Boilermaker . . . When the boats set out on the morning of May ninth while crowds of relieved citizens cheered them on their way, Jack and his crew quickly maneuvered for a place in the lead.

For days *The Pirate* kept far in the lead, taking the best of the food that farmers brought to the river bank, until she was finally overtaken. Then the fun was over. Food was scarce. The rains came and everyone was miserable. Word reached them that Coxey, the leader from Ohio, had been arrested in Washington for walking on the White House lawn. Each day the size of the army dwindled as men gradually deserted.

On Thursday, May twenty-fourth, about two weeks

after leaving Des Moines, the tattered remnants of the army camped on an island in the Mississippi River near Hannibal, Missouri. That night Jack lay in the swampy grass for a long time, thinking.

The fun was over. And adventure—he had seen enough of Mark Twain's country! Maybe Huck Finn liked this life, but it held no charm for a salt-water sailor.

Worst of all, he was traveling south when he should be going north. Up in Chicago, he was sure there were letters waiting for him. Eliza and his mother had promised to write him there. Probably they had sent money with which he could buy some decent clothes. He wanted to go to St. Joseph, Michigan, to visit his mother's sister, whom he had never seen. And then—on to New York and Washington!

There was a little skiff down on the river bank. I'll crawl out early and beat it for shore, he decided. Away from this mob, I can catch a freight going north.

Chapter **6**

In late June of 1894, New York was stifling. At night
hundreds of sweltering inhabitants of the Lower East
Side tenements emerged from their squalid, airless rooms
to roam the streets, sleep in parks, in doorways, on fire
escapes.

In a small park down near the City Hall during these
torrid days, Jack London, eighteen-year-old traveler and
sightseer, spent his late afternoons and nights. He had
discovered it soon after he rode into the city on a freight
train and had decided at once that it would be his head-
quarters. It had everything he needed: trees, grass,
benches to sit and sleep on, and people. Here in this
crowded place, he was reasonably sure that the police
would not jar him from slumber at night with the usual
tap of a club and the command, "Move on," that he had
learned to know and avoid.

His daily routine was simple. After a morning of sight-seeing and battering the drag for pickin's, he headed for the park. If the pickin's were good, he went first to one of the pushcart vendors who sold damaged copies of new books discarded by the publishers. In the park, he selected a choice bench near one of the little booths that dispensed ice-cold milk or buttermilk for a penny a glass. Then he settled down to pleasant hours of reading and drinking glass after glass of milk until twilight.

Before the benches became crowded for the night, he folded the coat of the gray suit that Aunt Mary Everhard had bought for him in St. Joseph, Michigan, and placed it under his head for a pillow. Curled up on the bench, waiting for sleep, he watched the people go by—watched and thought about them.

During the carefree mornings, while he explored the huge city from end to end, Jack was always caught up in the excitement of it. But at night, when pale, ragged children and spiritless, defeated men and women dragged past him, the city took on a fearful aspect. What would happen to these destitute people when winter came? he often wondered.

During the past year of unemployment, Oakland had been bad enough, he remembered. There, however, he had watched from the sidelines. But here he was one of the homeless ones, and for the first time he became truly aware of the suffering and hopelessness of this class of society.

If I wanted a job in New York, could I find one? he

sometimes asked himself. Some of the men who passed him must have seen better days, he was sure. The chief outward difference between them and him was his obvious good health—his bronzed skin and bulging muscles, his appearance of being well-fed. Though he had not been out of his clothes since he left Michigan, had slept in fields, hay mows, and boxcars, had ridden the rods and once had worked his way for a short run by passing coal on an engine, he did not yet have the look of permanent poverty that he saw everywhere around him.

But how long might it take him to acquire that look? And why, in a city of such obvious wealth and progress, were some people so rich and others so desperately, hopelessly poor?

For the first time in his life, questions like these began to trouble Jack London, though not deeply, and not for long. Each morning he wakened rested and cheerful, eager for any adventure that the new day might bring. There was so much of the country yet to see—Niagara Falls, Washington, D.C., New England. And when I've had enough, I'll head west, he told himself. No winters in New York for me!

One late afternoon, Jack swung south along Broadway, whistling softly as he headed for the little park. He had had a fine day. He tried to estimate the distance he had covered since dawn, and decided that he must have walked about ten miles.

His mind buzzed with all that he had seen and done. From the very tip of Manhattan Island, the Battery, he had wandered north for miles along the Hudson River, entranced by the great ships from all over the world that docked there. With a quick eye for sailors flush with pay, he had picked up enough handouts for a huge breakfast in a waterfront tavern. It wasn't every day that he could sit down to four eggs and cup after cup of Java!

That royal meal carried him along for a few more miles up the great river until he suddenly decided to cut east to tree-shaded Central Park. There he rested pleasantly on a bench and watched children sail toy boats at the edge of a little lake.

At last, aware that his pockets were empty, he set off down Broadway, the main drag. Pickin's were usually good, he had found, among the tall buildings and fashionable hotels, if he kept a sharp eye out for bulls and flashed his appealing, boyish smile. He had learned to edge up to a motherly-looking woman and tell a sad story of being stranded in New York on his way to visit his grandmother. That act was often good for a dime and sometimes even a quarter. He had to be careful, though. Once a sweet-faced little woman had screamed for the police.

When he had picked up nearly fifty cents, a good haul, there was still time to cut over to a new Free Library that he had found right off Fifth Avenue on Twentieth Street, and spend an hour browsing through strange and fascinating magazines. Now, as the afternoon grew late, he was headed contentedly for his little park to stake a claim on a bench for the night. At intervals he swung his rumpled coat from one shoulder to the other and mopped his sunburned face with his sleeve. His grimy, sodden shirt clung to his back and chest. Every few minutes, a trickle of perspiration coursed between his shoulder blades.

As he strolled along, he carried on a running argument with himself over how he should spend his money. Steak and Java were a quarter; but in this heat, he decided upon penny glasses of ice-cold milk instead. I could get a bath for a dime at the barber shop, he reminded himself, and wash out my shirt, too. But I'd just be wasting my money. Maybe tomorrow it'll be cooler, and then I'll clean up, he promised himself.

He knew what he really wanted. A new book. Across from City Hall he stopped a pushcart dealer and thumbed through the day's offerings of damaged volumes until his eyes caught a familiar name. Rudyard Kipling, one of his favorite authors. And here was a new story just off the press, *The Jungle Book*. What luck!

He tossed the vendor a dime, tucked the book under his arm, and headed across the street, his dry throat now crying for ice-cold buttermilk.

In the middle of the street in front of the City Hall, he noticed a crowd of perhaps fifty men watching something in their midst. Mildly curious, he, too, sauntered up to look. Down on the pavement, on hands and knees, were some ragged little street urchins, intent upon a lusty game of marbles.

Jack smiled, remembering the collection of agates that he had had when he, too, was a street urchin. He had bartered and traded until he had the best collection in the West End of Oakland. For a few seconds he stood in the crowd, and then was about to leave when one of the boys cried "Bull!"

Like a shot, the word sent them flying. Jack laughed and moved on toward the park. Ahead he saw the "bull," a big officer in a gray uniform, saunter down the street and then change his direction toward the park. The fifty men were now spread out, but Jack moved directly on, still heading for the buttermilk stand. He was slipping a hand into his pocket searching for a penny to lay on the counter when he realized that his path and the policeman's were going to cross.

Suddenly the officer lunged at him, striking him on the chest with both hands and sending his precious book and coat flying.

"What . . . ?" Jack stammered, trying to regain his balance.

In a second, he saw the dreaded club and felt it crash against his skull. He reeled back while the pavement rose and fell before his eyes. And then, with the instinct born in earlier scrapes with the law, he ran. On and on he ran, his head throbbing, his feet staggering. Even when he heard no sound except the pounding of his own feet and head, he ran.

Somewhere in an alley he stopped, leaned against a building, and ran his fingers over his scalp. There was no blood, only a large lump under his thick hair. Gradually the dizziness and nausea left him as his mind searched for reasons.

Why? Why? he asked himself. He was a free American, walking into a free park in the city of New York. He was committing no crime, doing no wrong.

There seemed to be only one answer. He *looked* like a bum, a member of the lowest stratum of society. The policeman had to show his authority, and so he hit the first unwashed head that he saw.

For a few minutes, Jack stood in the alley, trying to collect his thoughts. His pleasant days in New York were at an end. He couldn't go back to the park. He didn't want to go! The only thing to do was clear out, go where the air was clean and beautiful.

Niagara Falls! That was the place. He turned in the direction of the railroad station, determined now to ride the next train out.

Two days later, in Niagara Falls, Jack London jumped down from the off side of a boxcar into hot afternoon sunshine. His shirt, streaked with dirt and perspiration, clung to his back, and his hair lay matted in wet ringlets above his fiery face.

He glanced furtively around and then dodged across the tracks to an overflowing water tank that he had spotted as the train slowed down. He thrust his head under a stream of cold, clear water, swallowed great gulps of it, and let it pour over his steaming face and neck. But when a yardman began to move toward him, he shook his head like a spaniel and took off toward the main drag.

Falling in with a group of tourists, he followed the signs that pointed to the falls. In school books, when he was a boy, he had read about this great spectacle, and now he was about to see it! Soon his ears picked up the thunder of downrushing water and he pushed eagerly ahead. At last, across a grassy park, he sighted great clouds of mist rising and falling, catching the sunlight and spraying it out in rainbow hues. The thunder grew louder, and he broke into a run.

On the mist-filled promontory, he skidded to a stop and gazed down, at once enthralled by the plunging, boiling waters, the rainbow lights, the rolling, drifting mist. People jostled him, but he did not move. In all his travels over the ocean, through mountains and plains, down rivers, into great cities, he had never seen such beauty, and he could not take his eyes from it. In a few short minutes, all the bitterness that he had felt since he left New York was washed away in the rushing water.

In a dream, Jack wandered for hours along the edge of the falls, viewing them from every possible angle.

As the sun dropped lower and the colors deepened, each subtle change delighted him. Vaguely, he knew that he was hungry, but he stayed on while a full moon came up to add its shadowy enchantment.

At last when the moon slipped behind a cloud and everyone else had left, he turned reluctantly away. If he had dared, he would have slept on the grass of the park. But one blow of a club had made him wary. And so he wandered out of town, his head still full of the magic he had seen. In a field, he threw himself onto the ground and fell asleep at once.

At dawn, Jack was wakened by sharp pangs of hunger, but he lay on his back a little longer, thinking. The sun was barely up, and so it must be no later than five o'clock, he decided. To batter the "privates," the homes, for breakfast, he would have to wait until eight o'clock when the men were off at work, he knew. But in the intervening hours, he could go back to the falls and see them in the solitude of sunrise. That might be the very best time of all!

Quickly he got to his feet, brushed the dew from his clothes, and swung happily down the road.

As he entered the town, he noticed that he was not the only person awake. Three men were walking toward him. Stiffs, he thought. Out looking for breakfast. The first rays of the sun were in his eyes, and he couldn't be sure. But as the men drew close and he could see them clearly, a sudden chill froze his spine. The two men on the outside were stiffs, all right, but the one in the middle was in uniform. A bull!

It was too late to run. He tried to pass, but the officer stopped him.

"What hotel are you stopping at?" he asked.

"I—I just arrived," Jack answered.

"Well, come along. The judge wants to see you."

He motioned to a position directly in front of him.

Jack had no choice. Down the street he marched, while his mind seethed with resentment. He hadn't done a thing in this town to cause his arrest, hadn't begged, hadn't even slept within the city limits. He'd tell that judge a thing or two!

In the court room he was lined up with fifteen others. One by one they were called up. Each case required about fifteen seconds. The judge called a name. The bailiff replied, "Vagrancy, your honor." "Thirty days," pronounced the judge.

Jack's blood boiled. When his turn came, he'd threaten them, demand a lawyer and jury. He was an American citizen and knew his rights!

"John London," the judge called.

"Vagrancy, your honor," said the bailiff.

"Thirty days."

"Your honor . . ." Jack protested.

"Shut up!" the judge snapped and called the next name.

The bailiff pushed Jack into his seat. His trial was over.

The next few hours for Jack were filled with visions of damage suits, sensational newspaper headlines, exposure of injustices, as the authorities heaped one indignity after another upon him and his fellow prisoners. He was handcuffed to a tall, powerful Negro and lined up in a double line, while a long chain was run through the handcuffs and locked front and rear. A chain gang! They were marched to the railway station, loaded into a car, later taken off and put onto a street car, walked again, and finally herded into the Erie County Penitentiary near Buffalo, New York.

More indignities followed. Heads were shaved, clothing taken away, prison stripes issued. Then, with his hands on the shoulders of the man ahead, Jack learned to walk the prison lock step through the gray corridors. He looked up, counted the six tiers of cells, saw the guards with Winchester rifles, and knew that for thirty days there was no escape. But just wait until he got out!

The next thirty days changed eighteen-year-old Jack London from a happy-go-lucky boy to a man. Along with the soft down that was shaved from his face for the first time went many of the convictions that he had cherished all his life: that a man was innocent unless proved guilty; that every American had the right of habeas corpus; that penitentiaries were for convicted felons. He knew without a doubt that he was now a member of the lowest class of society. He was down in the cellar, where he might remain if he didn't watch his step. There was no one to turn to now, not his father or mother or even Eliza, for in two days he learned that the letters he tried to smuggle out to them never got beyond the prison walls.

Gradually, as he watched the brutality of the guards and listened to stories from other prisoners of horrors they had seen, all thought of revenge and restitution left him. He wanted only to live through the thirty days and get out and away from this place as fast as possible while he was still strong enough. Already he was growing weak on a diet of bread and water after hard labor all day in the prison yard.

One night he lay in his narrow cell, thinking. Among the five hundred men locked in cells in this hall of the penitentiary were some first-timers as innocent as he. But most of the other inmates were hardened criminals, degenerates, physical or mental wrecks. There was another small group, however, the trusties, hallmen. They did no hard labor, had the freedom of the halls, and obtained extra portions of bread and sometimes meat.

The only way to survive, Jack knew, was to become a trusty. But how? Not by good behavior, he was sure, but evidently by knowing the right people.

Jack's mind kept working through the problem. That other fellow named Jack who had been arrested along with him. He was a short, heavy-muscled three-timer, but he had already become a hallman. In most ways he was a brute, but there was a shred of kindness in him that might be cultivated. He knew the ropes, all right. On the way in, he had passed along some tips on how to smuggle a few personal belongings past the guards.

The next time he came along, Jack London was ready. He had smuggled in a pouch of tobacco, and hallman Jack had a pipe. The gift of a pipeful of tobacco was the trick. The next day, he was let out of his cell to become a hallman and a grafter along with the others, exchanging bread for tobacco and tobacco for meat, smuggling letters from one part of the prison to another. Scrupulously he lived by the law of the inmates, kept out of trouble, ate better, and carefully nurtured the friendship with three-timer Jack, on whom his well-being depended.

When the day of release finally came, the two Jacks left together. Jack London pulled his cap low over his shaven head and kept an eye out for the police. He had seen too many men hauled in again the day after their release on the same count—vagrancy—to take chances. He had only one wish, to get far away from Buffalo as fast as possible.

But his burly companion clung to him, spouting his plans. The two should team up in a life of petty crime. He already had a couple of jobs lined up.

As they walked down the street, begging for a few cents here and there, Jack's mind worked fast. His companion was not above turning him in if he tried to shake him. He couldn't risk a slip-up now.

"I'm thirsty," he said as they passed a saloon. "Let's talk this over."

Inside, over three-cent beer, Jack pretended the greatest interest. When he heard the hoot of an engine, he called for a second beer.

"Be back in a minute," he muttered.

He slipped out the rear door, leaving his unsuspecting jailmate with two foaming mugs. And then he raced through alleys to the freight yard and swung under a train headed south.

As Jack wandered down through Pennsylvania during August, sleeping in fields and haymows, begging for food as he went along, some of his old carefree, happy spirit returned. He was still strong and healthy; adventure lay ahead. And yet the things he had seen and heard in New York and Buffalo made him think hard about the world he lived in and his place in it.

Time after time, the scenes of brutality in the penitentiary came back to haunt him: a man beaten by the guards for a few dollars that he had managed to smuggle in; a slow-witted inmate tormented until his mind broke completely; hands that reached hungrily for an extra portion of bread crushed by a club. . . . These and many other scenes he could not push from his memory. They rode with him wherever he went, making him wary of strangers, always on the lookout for his enemies, the bulls, as he moved south.

One hot afternoon he floated lazily in the Susquehanna River. On the bank, his shirt that he had washed fluttered from a twig.

Gradually the cool water swept away the feverish heat engendered by a morning on top of a mail car, and he frolicked in the river for a while, scrubbing the grime and perspiration from his body, diving into the green depths and spouting long streams of water into the air. He rubbed a hand over his stubble of hair and tried to estimate the length of it. Half an inch, maybe, he decided. Before long he could go into a library and take off his cap without shame. And in a couple of months, his hair would be long enough so that he could go home and face his mother.

At last he climbed out onto the river bank, swept himself dry with the palms of his hands, and pulled on his shirt and trousers. Then he lay down under a huge oak tree and rubbed his bare feet in the cool, thick grass. Overhead, a bluejay scolded him, and he answered with a saucy chirp. At his feet, water lapped softly against the bank.

If I had a raft, he thought, I could float all the way to Washington, D.C. For a while his mind fashioned a raft of driftwood and bits of rope and wire, and then gave up. A few weeks on the Des Moines and Mississippi Rivers on a flatboat had been enough for one summer, he decided.

He reached for the book that lay in the grass beside

him and riffled through it to a dog-eared page. He sighed. Most of the books he had picked up lately in rubbish cans or on penny counters in secondhand stores were novels about handsome men and beautiful women who lived in fine, clean homes, drove in shiny carriages, and had beautiful thoughts that they expressed in gracious noble words. There was a time when a book like this one would have amused him for a whole afternoon. But now it only made him think of all the people he knew— the people who didn't live such splendid lives.

He dropped the book into the grass and tucked his hands under his head. And then painfully he tried to line up into a pattern some of the perplexing, often frightening, thoughts that had been tumbling about in his head. All the people he saw as he traveled over the country seemed to be divided into classes, but somehow he didn't fit into any of them.

There was the lowest class, the cellar of society, that he, Jack London, without realizing what was happening to him, had fallen into. But he wasn't going to stay there! Then directly above it but not very far, was the working class. "I know all about that one," he muttered to the bluejay. "I was born into it. But how do I get out?"

He rubbed his hand over the splendid muscles of his right arm. A muscle merchant, that's what I was. Selling my muscles for ten cents an hour. And when muscles wear out, what then? A picture of his father sitting across the table from him, staring at his idle hands, flashed before Jack. Pictures of worn-out older men he had met on the road paraded through his mind. They had no more muscles to sell.

It's pretty simple, after all, he finally decided. For food and shelter, everybody sells something. Laborers sell their muscles until they wear out. Merchants—they sell clothes and food and books and things. With the money they make, they replenish their stock. They're in another class—they can live on the parlor floor of society.

He thought for a while longer. There was another group that he hadn't accounted for. He picked up the book again and turned it over in his hands. The fellow who wrote this book, for instance. Teachers. Librarians like that nice white-haired lady in Oakland. What did they sell? Why, their brains, of course. And brains weren't like muscles. They didn't wear out.

Suddenly Jack sat up in the grass and hugged his knees as the answer flashed into his mind. Brains! They were the *only* things that didn't wear out or didn't have to be replenished. They grew better and stronger as the years went on, if people used them and educated them.

He ran his fingers over his close-cropped head. There were brains there. He knew it. Hadn't he won a prize for writing a story when he was only seventeen? The second and third prize winners were both university students, he remembered. And books—he had read hundreds of them since he was a kid.

Maybe I can't get up to the parlor floor, he thought. But I could have a try at the attic!

Quickly he pulled on his shoes and got to his feet. The thing to do was have a plan. Go to high school. Then the University of California. Read the right books, not just any old thing that came to hand. Study grammar.

The sun was dropping low as he strode off across the field toward a farmhouse where he might get a handout. More lighthearted than he had been in many months, he continued to spin his plans. There was still much to see in the East before he returned, but he'd have to hurry. Washington, D.C., Baltimore, New York City again, Boston—and then home across Canada before the snows came.

Work? Of course he'd work again to pay for an education. But now things would be different. He wouldn't be working for just room and grub and Sundays at Blair Park. He'd be working for something with a future to it!

Chapter **7**

Jack London tilted back his chair, rubbed his hands over his full stomach, and grinned at his mother.

"Best setdown I've had since I left Winnipeg, Ma," he said.

"Setdown?" She eyed him questioningly through her thick lenses.

"Sure. You know—at a table with things like these on it." He waved a knife and fork under her nose.

"Hmpf," his mother responded. "Your appetite hasn't changed, but your table manners have. Put down that knife and fork!"

Jack obeyed and then fumbled in his pocket for a plug of chewing tobacco, slipped the knife under the table, and surreptitiously cut off a small piece. He popped it into the side of his mouth and sighed.

"I wish Pa was at home. I've been thinking about him all the way down from Vancouver, wondering how he was. Sure glad to know he's feeling better and able to work. But I still can't get over it—my father a *bull!*"

Eliza stamped her foot. "You *stop* using that word around here, Jack London," she commanded. "Your father is *not* a bull. He has a very respectable job as deputy policeman and you've just eaten food that his wages bought. So keep still about 'bulls' when he gets home, do you hear?"

Jack hung his head and chewed pensively on his tobacco. "I'm sorry, Eliza," he apologized.

The kitchen was silent as Jack strove to push the past seven months into the back of his consciousness. But it wasn't easy. He had left Oakland on a boy's lark that he thought might last for only a month or two. Now, much later, he was back, wiser in the ways of men, harder in manner, rougher in language. The things he had seen and done—many of them he couldn't tell anyone, not even his family. They were bad enough at the time; but here, as he sat at the familiar worn kitchen table with his mother and sister, they were unthinkable.

Jack's eyes roamed around the kitchen, saw the same old oilcloth on the table, the old stove, an iron sink in the corner. And yet this was a different kitchen from the one he had left in April. His mother had moved again, just as he had predicted, and he'd had to find out from a neighbor that she had gone only three blocks to the north.

But for the life of him he couldn't see what was more

desirable about this place. All the houses they had lived in were much the same. A little more or less paint, a little more or less room, but they were all small, square, unadorned workmen's cottages. Inside, he could hardly tell the difference.

"You going to settle down now?" his mother asked— she who could not settle down anywhere for long.

"Yeh," Jack answered. "I've got plans."

He saw a look pass between Eliza and his mother.

"Since the railroad strike, they're taking on more deputy policemen, and the pay's good," his mother ventured.

Jack pounced to his feet and paced back and forth across the kitchen. They didn't understand! They'd *never* understand if he explained for a month. He—Jack London—a strikebreaker!

He pounded the table with a hard brown fist and shouted: "You'll just have to get it straight. I'll wash windows, mow lawns, beat carpets. I'll do any kind of decent, honest labor for room and grub. But I won't be a—a—"

His eyes fell on Eliza's tense jaw and he dropped his voice.

"Anyway," he added, "I can't take a regular job. I'm going to high school."

For once Flora London was speechless. At last she gasped, "Have you lost your senses?"

Jack rubbed his hands over his eyes. Suddenly he was

99

very tired. He could walk out of this house, out into the grassy hills, and drop asleep in a moment. But here he must explain, argue for the right to make up his own mind.

Only, he didn't want to leave home again. Leaving home was not a part of his plan.

"No, Ma," he answered, trying to keep the roughness out of his voice. "I've seen a lot of this country and the people in it since I left here last spring. And I've learned something. The only way for me to get ahead is to educate myself. Brain-merchants don't have to stand in the lines at mills and factories. I'm going to high school and then to the university, and don't try to stop me, Ma."

In the silence that followed, Eliza moved slowly across the room, a look of love and understanding in her dark eyes. She put her arms around his big, hard shoulders and kissed his sun-baked cheek. And then she leaned back and looked at him, puzzled.

"What's that you've been chewing, Jack?" she asked.

Her brother's face flushed under its coat of tan and he glanced away.

"Oh . . . just a little quid . . . keeps my teeth from hurting."

"Well, spit it out!"

Jack looked toward the sink.

"No! Out there!" She pointed to the door.

Meekly, Jack went out the kitchen door and returned in a moment, wiping his lips with the back of his hand.

Eliza stood under the light. Since he was a baby, she had commanded and he had obeyed. Now, as she crooked her finger toward him, he went to her.

"Open your mouth, Jack. Let me see your teeth."

Obediently he opened. In the harsh light his sister looked, and then he heard a long, slow gasp.

"Your teeth! Where did they go? You lost two in that shipboard fight, but the others— Let's see. One . . . two . . . Must be four or five more. And the rest are full of holes!"

Jack closed his mouth and grinned. "Guess it was in Iowa—can't remember just where. I had a toothache. A real bad one. The fellows held me down. It took four of 'em—Boilermaker and Scotty and a couple more. The army dentist yanked 'em out."

He rubbed his jaw as he remembered. "Hurt like— like blazes at first, but then I felt better. When I got another toothache in Buffalo, one of the stiffs told me about chewing tobacco. Works fine."

Eliza frowned. "Well, no brother of mine is going to high school with teeth like that, and chewing tobacco, too. I'll find a dentist for you tomorrow. You've got to have those holes filled and some new teeth, too."

"You mean false teeth? Those things cost plenty!"

Eliza put on her coat and hat, preparing to leave.

"You've got to have them, that's all. I'll pay, if you'll promise not to chew tobacco any more."

Jack hesitated. He'd been chewing tobacco for several

months, borrowing from and sharing with any casual friend of the road. He'd learned to like it. But Eliza was right. He couldn't chew tobacco around the high school and so he might as well give it up along with cussing and a lot of other things from the old life.

He pulled the plug from his pocket and handed it to her with an impish smile.

"It's a bargain," he said. "You get tobacco. I get teeth."

Jack London wasted no time in carrying out his plans. The next morning he pulled on the old blue suit that he had left behind in April and dashed the more than two miles to the big three-story Oakland High School at Twelfth and Clay. Never had he stepped inside that building. He had never even thought of going inside!

Six years, he told himself. I've wasted six whole years. Why, I could have been more than halfway through the university by now!

But no matter. He would make up that lost time— learn twice as fast as soon as he got the hang of studying again. Set up a table in his room and work every night to catch up with the class that was already two months ahead of him.

In the office, the astonished principal listened to the eager plans of this strange, overgrown boy in the wrinkled, shabby suit. His eyes swept over the tousled mop of hair, the shining deep-set eyes in the sunburned face, the strong, jutting jaw, the muscular neck and shoulders. He glanced out into the corridor as his pupils passed by to their classes—boys in knee pants, girls with pigtails and hair ribbons.

"This is very irregular," he said at last. "The term is half over. You would have to make up a great deal. Algebra . . . French . . . They would be very difficult, especially since you say you must take part-time jobs besides. I really don't believe . . ."

Jack's eyes clouded and he set his jaw. This fellow wasn't going to stop him. Nobody was. He laid a clenched fist on the desk and stared at it. Then slowly he pushed his hand into his pocket. In this new life he couldn't settle things with his fists. He had to use his head.

He spread his lips in a wide, appealing smile.

"But I *can* go, can't I, Mr. McChesney? I mean—this is a free high school, isn't it?"

"Y—yes. So long as you do your work and obey the rules."

Jack got to his feet and pulled his cap from his pocket. "Well, then, I want to get the books so I can start right in tonight. Algebra and French and English grammar and history are what I want to learn."

The next morning, Jack bounded up the steps of the high school and swung down the long hall toward the algebra classroom to which he had been assigned. He

103

stopped in the doorway and looked around at the rows of desks, each with its inkwell and pen tray, at the blackboards that covered the walls, the erasers and chalk, the teacher's desk.

A quick smile brightened his face. This is it, he thought. The place where I belong—where I can learn the answers.

He glanced over the desks again, selected the last one in the first row, and headed toward it. Dropping his books onto the top, he slumped into the seat and spread his feet comfortably out in front of him. Then he licked his thumb and quickly riffled through page after page of his penny tablet. Now and then he stopped, frowned, and made a mark or two on a figure-filled page. When he came to a clean sheet, he opened his algebra book and set to work.

Boys and girls began to wander in, chattering and giggling, but he did not look up. Pencil in one hand and finger pointing to a line in the book, he worked steadily through the list of problems. Once he laughed aloud, slammed his fist onto the desk, and then wrote more furiously than before.

A gong sounded, and a crowd of noisy students pushed through the door and scrambled for seats. A tall, dark-haired woman took her place behind the desk, picked up a long wooden pointer, and rapped for order.

"Attention please!" she commanded as she took up her classbook and began to call the roll.

"Adams."

"Present."

"Allen."

"Present."

In the quiet of the room, as the roll-taking went on, Jack slowly raised his eyes from his book. So this was the teacher. She looked all right. He swung an arm over the back of his seat and turned around. There were forty or fifty young boys and girls in the seats behind him, and the eyes of every one of them were staring at him.

Jack felt the blood slowly rise to his cheeks, but he stared back coolly before he brought his attention again to the teacher. Let them gawk. He was as smart as they were.

I'll show 'em, he promised himself. Just give me time and I'll work any problem in the book faster than any of 'em.

The teacher had finished the roll call and was puzzling over a slip of paper.

"London," she pronounced.

Jack's throat went dry.

"Present," he mumbled.

With relief he watched her put the slip of paper into the back of her classbook and open the text.

Jack forgot about the staring eyes as he listened intently to the explanation of a group of problems on page seventy-three. For hours the night before he had worked at nothing but algebra, placing x and y in neat equations according to the directions in the book, searching into his childhood for rules of multiplication and division. Methodically he had moved down one page and then the next as he worked each problem. First he sat at the rough old table that he had moved from the back porch into his room. Later, driven to his bed by the cold of a November night, he had continued, wrapped in blankets and propped against pillows. Sometime long after midnight he had fallen asleep while the light still burned.

He had covered twenty-five pages, but this stuff on page seventy-three— It was beyond him. He shuffled through the intervening pages. Somewhere in all that puzzle of letters and figures were the terms that this teacher used so glibly. In a few more nights he'd find them. Maybe, too, he would catch on to the reason for putting x's and y's on paper and trying to find what they equaled.

Reluctantly Jack took his place at the blackboard with the others, vaguely conscious of his long baggy spring-bottom trousers among the neat knee pants of his smaller classmates. But in a moment his attention was glued to the problem on the board as the teacher moved up behind him. He didn't want to talk about it in front of everybody.

"I'll get the hang of it in a few days, Miss," he said gruffly.

When she moved on he glanced at the problems on both sides of him and tried to write something that looked all right. His chalk squeaked against the board. As he finished and put it down next to the eraser, it clung, damp and slippery, to his hand.

Jack's determination to catch up with and surpass his classmates did not waver as the weeks flew by. After school and on Saturdays he went from house to house searching for work of any kind that would pay his board at home and give him a little extra for school supplies and other necessities. Long into the night he studied.

One Sunday morning in January he dropped by his sister's home to repay the last dollar of the money he had borrowed for his schoolbooks. Since the winter rains had started, jobs were harder to find. But he had had the good luck on Saturday to find a woman who wanted someone to beat carpets, wash windows, and polish floors. The rain had held off for a day and he had worked from early morning until dark. Now he could repay that last dollar.

He tapped on the kitchen door, sniffed the Sunday roast cooking in the oven, and walked in. He found Eliza bent over the open oven door, a big basting spoon in her hand, a strand of damp hair across her flushed forehead. As he looked at her, a series of pictures flashed through his mind: Eliza bent over a stove on the ranch at Livermore, in the dingy kitchen of that potato farm on the coast, on the truck farm in Alameda. Eliza always working for others, for Flora, her stepmother, and then at sixteen for her middle-aged husband, Captain Shepard, and his two children who weren't much younger than she. Now, besides all her other responsibilities, she was partner with her husband in a pension-claim business. Never anyone her own age to have fun with. Seldom any fun at all. No wonder her face was serious and already old.

But she was never too busy or too tired to listen to his plans and always willing to spare some of her earnings for him.

"Hm. Looking for a setdown?" she quipped.

Jack laughed and dangled a silver dollar in front of her. "This stiff's able to pay," he said. "Do you know, I haven't thought about those setdowns for a long time. I wonder how I ever got up the nerve to batter the gates."

Eliza dropped into a chair. "Sit down, Jack. I don't see you much any more. Let me have a look."

She reached across the table and pushed the hair from his forehead. "You look peaked. Circles under your eyes."

She glanced down at his hands.

"Why are you wearing those straps on your wrists?"

Jack loosened the old leather straps and laid them on the table. "I don't wear 'em much any more," he answered. "But yesterday I was beating carpets and hauling things around all day. Jobs are hard to find and I have to take what I can get."

Carefully he flexed his wrists and winced. "Wrists don't hurt too much any more, but these straps—it's a good thing for me to put 'em on once in a while. Remind myself of what I might be doing now if I hadn't gone away and started thinking."

Eliza's brow puckered. "You're really serious about this studying, Jack?" she asked. "You're planning to keep on with it?"

"Keep on! Of course I am. I've caught up with the class already. That was easy. But there's so much more to learn that isn't in the school books. You'll never believe it, Eliza, but last year I met plenty of stiffs who knew a lot more than the high school teachers do. You should have listened to that bunch in Baltimore argue about stuff I'd never heard of—philosophy and economics and science. They'd talk about fellows named Spencer and Kant and Nietzsche and then they'd bear down on a free library and look up all sorts of stuff and go on arguing. It was great!"

He rubbed a hand over his face as he remembered.

"Only trouble was—I didn't know what they were talking about. Seemed as if I hadn't learned a thing in nearly nineteen years. Just wasted my time hanging around the waterfront with a bunch of ignorant bums or picking up girls in a candy store."

Eliza kept her eyes on his mobile face.

"But . . . It must be kind of lonesome for you over in that high school. I've seen those kids. They aren't like us. Their folks can afford to send them to high school and buy them nice clothes. Are they friendly?"

Jack flushed. "What do I care if they're friendly or not. I have to work. But I'll show 'em. I've written a story that's going to be published in the school paper, the *Aegis,* about the sealing fleet at Bonin Island. And I'm working on some tramp stories that'll make 'em sit up, I tell you."

Eliza shook her head in troubled silence.

"Well, then," she said at last, "you've got to have steady money. You're wasting too much time hunting for jobs and walking all that way to school and back. I'll get a bicycle for you. And I know Jacob Winkler, the janitor. Maybe I can pull some strings and get you on as a helper."

The new bicycle, mastered after a series of harrowing spills, and a regular job as janitor's helper in the school made a difference in Jack's life. Each morning in the fog-shrouded dawn he sped off across town, books and lunch pail strapped to his shoulders, cap pulled low, baggy trousers clipped tight above his ankles. Before the first bell rang, he swept, mopped, and dusted while his head swarmed with equations and French verbs and the dates of battles. After school he rushed through his chores again until his quota of work was finished.

And then he was free, with an hour or two for himself before he must light the lamp on his bicycle and pedal home for supper. In the early dusk he turned his wheel away from the indifferent schoolyard and the memory of laughing, carefree voices, and headed toward the little library only two blocks away.

Each time he parked his bicycle in the rack and bounded up the steps, the warmth and friendliness of that haven in the center of Oakland reached out to him. As he passed the magazine and newspaper section on the first floor and tiptoed up the circular stairs to the quiet room on the second floor with its wall of books that reached to the ceiling, its tables and chairs and lamps already glowing, he knew that here he would find people who were doing as he was—filling their minds. The shabby and the well-dressed shared the same tables, read the same books. No one stared at him. And behind the central desk with its small vase of flowers and a display of the latest books sat the new librarian, Mr. Bamford, immaculate in high starched collar and neat dark suit, every white hair in place.

Sometimes as he swung through the door, it seemed to Jack that the librarian had actually been waiting for him. A sparkle would come into the blue eyes behind their spectacles, and a little smile would crease the corners of his mouth. Often he would reach under his desk and bring out a book. "Here's something that may interest you," he might say. Or "I wonder if you've seen this?" Sometimes it was a small book of poems. Or perhaps, when he found that Jack was interested in the

111

social problems of the world, he might hand him a volume by Ruskin or Carlyle.

Whatever it was, Jack accepted it gratefully as he returned the book that he had read the night before, after his school work was finished.

The warm feeling followed him to a favorite table in the corner where he could spread out his schoolbooks and set to work. Now and then, as he finished one lesson and started on another, he looked up at faces bent over books, listened to murmured queries for information, or sought a glance from the young assistant, Fred Jacobs.

A strange friendship had started up between these two young men; and often, as Jack pedaled home through the dusk, he thought and wondered about the slight, blond fellow who moved quietly around the library putting books back into place, answering questions, and offering help to any puzzled reader. Mr. Bamford had introduced them one rainy afternoon when the library was nearly empty, and in the short conversation that followed, Jack had learned that Fred Jacobs, too, was working his way through high school by assisting in the library during the day and attending classes at night. He, too, wanted to go to the university. But a fellow like this—from his skinny muscles and smooth hands, anybody could see he had never done a day's hard labor in his life—why was he friendly when the high school students weren't?

Maybe he doesn't fit into one of the classes of society

any better than I do, Jack decided one day. Maybe, like me, he's decided that his brains are the only things that will get him anywhere.

One day, Jack and Fred left the library at the same time. A soft mist was falling, and at the door Fred started to tuck a book under his coat.

"What's that you're reading?" Jack asked.

Fred pulled out the book and opened it. "It's a new book about photography."

"Photography?"

"Yes. Are you interested in it?"

Jack shook his head. Photography. Picture taking. He'd never even thought of it.

"It's very interesting," Fred Jacobs went on, his serious face lighting up as he talked. "I've been developing my own pictures, doing some experimenting with the chemicals I use. When you have time, I'd like to have you come over to see some of my best things. That is, if you'd care to."

Jack flushed and a new shyness left him searching for words. The last friend he had made in Oakland was Louis Shattuck, and he hadn't seen him for a year. Even then, he had never been invited into Louis's home. He didn't even know where it was! And now this new fellow with his quiet good manners and speech was opening a door to him.

"I—I'd sure like that. I don't know anything about chemistry yet. But I'm going to learn."

Fred waved a hand as they parted on the steps and Jack awkwardly raised his hand, too. And then he threw himself onto his bicycle and pedaled furiously toward home.

Chapter **8**

Throughout the spring of 1895, when Jack went into the library he looked first for Fred Jacobs before he took his accustomed seat and opened his books. Conversations there were usually brief and whispered. But sometimes as they left the building—Jack for home and an evening of study and writing for the *Aegis,* and Fred for night classes at the high school—they talked at greater length.

Sometimes Fred brought photographs that he had recently developed—pictures of his girl, Bess Maddern, slender and dark-haired, who also hoped to go to the university. There were pictures of other friends, too, Ted Applegarth and his sister Mabel.

"I've been telling them about you, Jack," Fred said one warm May evening. "They want to meet you. Ted's going to a cramming school over in Alameda, Anderson's Academy, so that he can enter the university in the fall. And Mabel's already taking some university classes. You'd like them."

Jack examined a picture of an ethereal blond girl in a ruffled white dress and then handed it back to Fred.

"I—I don't know," he said as he jerked his cap from his pocket and crammed it onto his tousled hair. "I'm just starting high school and I don't know very much yet. They'll think I'm pretty dumb—nineteen years old and only a high school freshman. Besides I—I—"

How could he explain about the other things? The only clothes he had were the ones he wore. And even if he had a suit like Fred's and a white shirt and a necktie, what would he say to girls like Bess Maddern and Mabel Applegarth?

"Dumb?" Fred laughed. "Well, I guess not! Think of all those places you've seen—Japan, New York, Niagara Falls. . . ."

Suddenly Jack began to laugh. Each time he tried to answer Fred, the thought of describing the chain gang on its way to the Erie County Penitentiary to that dainty little blond girl seemed so ridiculous that laughter bubbled up again and he could not stop. At last, as he leaned over his bicycle and began to adjust the light, he sobered enough to answer.

"Yeh," he said. "I could tell 'em about Niagara Falls. It was sure a pretty sight."

"Well, we'll fix something up soon. Maybe we could

go out into the hills on our bicycles some Sunday and have a picnic. As soon as school's out, you'll need a change from all the studying you've been doing."

When Fred waved good-by and turned in the direction of the high school, Jack slipped onto his bicycle and hurried toward East Oakland. He had a lot of work to do to prepare for end-of-the-year examinations. English grammar was the worst. Those double negatives that the teacher kept talking about! Nearly everybody he knew said "can't hardly"—everybody except Fred Jacobs and Mr. Bamford and the fellows who wrote books. But it was still hard to remember why it was supposed to be wrong.

As Jack dodged through the busy streets, however, his thoughts turned impatiently away from the high school and the routine of his classes there. Two more years before he would be ready for the university up at Berkeley. By that time Fred and his friends would be far ahead of him. He'd be twenty-five years old before he would graduate. Meanwhile his father was growing older and more feeble. He might have to take on the care of the family any day.

As he leaned his bicycle against the back porch he wondered for the hundredth time why it was that he, who wanted an education so much, should find it so hard to get while most of his classmates, who didn't seem to care whether they learned anything or not, should have such an easy time of it.

Late the next afternoon, as Jack was finishing his study hour in the library, he noticed another young man about his age wandering aimlessly among the shelves of books. He seemed to be waiting for someone. Now and then, as they passed, he spoke to Fred Jacobs in a friendly way. There was something about this fellow that puzzled Jack, and out of the corner of his eye he watched. Perhaps it was his coat, which seemed slightly different from anything Jack had seen, or the way he carried himself, as though he might bow to someone at any moment.

But soon Jack became absorbed with the translation of a particularly difficult French sentence, and he forgot about him.

At six o'clock, as he hurried out the door into the bright west sunlight, he raised his eyes toward the bay and the Golden Gate and filled his lungs with the tangy salt air. In another week school would be over for the summer. He'd have to hustle for jobs to pay his board at home and save up for more school books in the fall, he knew. But maybe . . . maybe . . . he could fix up his little old skiff and get out onto the water now and then for a day of fishing and reading!

And then he looked down toward the street and saw Fred Jacobs beckoning to him. Beside Fred stood the stranger that he had noticed in the library, and suddenly Jack knew who he was—the fellow whose picture Fred had shown him, the pretty girl's brother!

A cold fog of self-consciousness enveloped Jack. He shifted his books from one arm to the other and shoved a hand into his pocket before he moved slowly down the steps.

"Here's somebody who wants to meet you," Fred called. "Ted Applegarth."

As Jack reached the bottom step, Ted extended his hand. Jack flushed, shifted his books again, and the two shook hands solemnly.

"How do you do?" Ted Applegarth said in a firm, crisp voice that left Jack almost speechless. He had a strange way of talking, all right.

"Pleased to meet you," Jack mumbled and retrieved his hand.

Fred laughed pleasantly. "Don't let Ted's accent bother you, Jack. He's a jolly old Englishman, and after you get used to all this formal stuff, you'll find he's a good fellow."

Jack's face broke into its natural happy grin. His false teeth, which often bothered him, he had left at home, but the Englishman did not appear to notice.

"Fred talks about you so often that we have all been eager to meet you. He says that you have traveled a great deal and are preparing for the university."

Jack frowned. "Yeh," he said. "But I won't be ready for a long time."

"You ought to try Anderson's," Ted suggested. "It's an excellent academy and will get you ready in no time

119

at all. I've persuaded Fred to have a try at it next year."
He waited expectantly.

Jack's face brightened. "Do you suppose . . . ? Would they take a fellow like me?"

Fred cleared his throat. "Of course they'd take you, Jack. But—well, it's expensive. I've saved up some money and I'm going to work longer hours during the summer. I figure that I can just about make it by fall."

Jack shifted his feet, slowly wound the strap around his books, and fumbled with the buckle.

"Guess that leaves me out," he mumbled as he swung his books over his shoulder. "I'll have to stick to the free high school."

As Fred and Ted moved on, calling promises of seeing him later, Jack stood beside his wheel for a moment, his fists clenching the handlebar. Some fellows had all the luck. They lived on the parlor floor of society and they could never really understand what it was like to live in the cellar or even the kitchen. Not even Fred, who worked long hours in the library for the luxury of an education, could imagine how it was to shovel coal for sixteen hours a day every day of the week to pay for the bare necessities of life.

On the Saturday evening after school closed for the summer, Jack was restless. With no lessons to prepare and no steady job as janitor's assistant, he must soon make the rounds of all the places he knew where work might be found. But this evening he was at loose ends. Briefly he thought of the candy store and wondered if Louis Shattuck was still around. But that part of his life was over. He wouldn't have anything to say to Louis after all these months.

Leaving his bicycle at home, he strolled along Foothill Boulevard to Lake Merritt, stood for a while on the bridge over the little creek that connected the lake with San Francisco Bay, and then decided to go on over to the City Hall Park to see if the band had started its summer series of Saturday night concerts.

As he drew near the little triangular park with its gaily lighted bandstand and saw the groups of young girls in summer dresses strolling arm in arm, their parents seated on the benches, smart carriages passing slowly by waiting for the musicians to strike up, Jack's thoughts leaped across the country to that other City Hall Park where he had spent hot summer nights only a year before among hollow-eyed children and tattered, hopeless men and women.

There are plenty of hungry people in Oakland, too, he reminded himself, but they don't come up here to sleep. They stay on the other side of Seventh Street, where the police don't bother anybody.

The musicians were tuning their instruments, and a few blocks away Jack could hear the boom-boom of Salvation Army drums. He skirted the edge of the crowd and ambled across the gravel path toward the City Hall steps where a street speaker was haranguing a small group on the evils of child labor. On any good evening, someone would mount the steps and lecture anyone who would listen on the tyranny of the railroad companies, conditions among the working class, or any other subject that he felt needed airing. Jack often stopped to listen on his way to or from the library.

But tonight he was not in a mood for a lecture. He knew all about child labor. Hadn't he seen small children humped over the bobbins in the jute mill or crippled by the machines of the cannery? He looked around. Anyway, these weren't the people to talk to—these well-dressed people out to enjoy an evening of music. They weren't even listening. This fellow on the steps of the City Hall ought to be down on the other side of Seventh telling the working people to get together and demand better conditions for themselves and their children.

Jack was about to turn away when a voice stopped him.

"Not much of a speaker, is he?"

Where had he heard that clipped, precise speech before? He turned and surveyed the tall, gaunt, athletic-looking man beside him.

"You're an Englishman," he said.

In the flickering gaslight, he saw the man smile. "I am—or, I was," he replied. "Whitaker, Jim Whitaker." He held out his hand, and as Jack shook it he noticed that the man's clothes, though neatly pressed, were as shabby as his own.

"London. Jack London," he responded. "Pleased to meet you."

Whitaker went on: "I've noticed you around here now and then. Ever try to make a speech?"

Jack laughed. "Me? No! I'd be scared to death." He nodded toward the speaker. "That fellow's not much good. But some of 'em make a lot of sense. Trouble is, people don't listen. They just laugh and say, 'There's some crazy guy talking again. Ought to throw him in jail.' "

"Mm. True. But every little bit helps the cause. Some-body—like you, maybe—listens and gets interested. Perhaps you'd like to come to some of our Sunday night meetings down in Socialist Hall on Washington. You know the place?"

Jack nodded. He knew the small, run-down building with a meeting room upstairs that any group of people could rent for a small sum.

"Maybe I'll do that," he answered. "I have to work and study most of the time, but Sunday nights I get—" He stopped abruptly. He had almost said "lonesome."

"Fine," Jim Whitaker said. "Any Sunday."

Reluctantly Jack watched him disappear in the crowd. He would have liked to know more about this English-man who talked intelligently and yet was obviously poor. Why had he come to America? Was he out of work, like a lot of other people? He had brains—at least he seemed to have them. Couldn't he put his brains to work?

Maybe I'll find out, he thought, if I go to some of those Sunday night meetings.

Restless again, Jack wandered on down Broadway. The boom of Salvation Army drums, the jangle of tambourines, and the harsh sound of untrained voices raised in song grew louder. He hesitated at the corner of Tenth and Broadway. Across the street flared the torchlights of the Salvation Army meeting.

Suddenly a voice spoke out of the crowd. "Jack London! So good to see you again!"

Jack swung around.

"Ted Applegarth," he burst out, and then he felt the blood rise to his face. Ted had a girl with him. Under the street light Jack recognized her—slender, dark-haired Bess Maddern of the photographs.

Remembering Ted's "how-do-you-do" Jack managed to murmur the words in response to an introduction. He saw the girl's friendly, interested smile as she responded.

She's nice, he thought with surprise. Not a bit stuck up.

"Going anywhere in particular?" Ted asked. "We thought it might be fun to listen in on the Salvation Army meeting. Want to come along?"

Jack hesitated. Want to? Of course he did. But a Salvation Army meeting! He had sat through many of them with Louis Shattuck and various girls they had picked up, when they needed a free place to spend an evening.

"I—I don't think you'd like it very much," he said. "There's a lot of noise and singing, but . . ."

Bess thought for a moment. "There's a concert at the Congregational Church," she suggested. "Would you like to go there?"

Jack nodded quickly. He had no idea if he would like it or not, but it didn't matter. They really wanted him to join them!

Three abreast, they set out for the church across from the high school, Jack between the two new friends. At first he talked only when he was spoken to. Yes, he guessed he was glad that school was out. No, he hadn't heard how he came out on his examinations. Yes, he'd be looking for work so that he could go back to high school in the fall. But soon he was asking questions, too, and entering into the conversation as though he had known them for a long time.

When they reached the church, the concert had already started. They tiptoed into a back pew, Bess first, and then Jack, pushed firmly ahead by Ted. Someone played the piano, a group of men sang, and then a woman played a violin. But Jack scarcely heard any of it. He was conscious only of the two people beside him and of himself between them. Incredibly, in a few minutes, he had walked out of one world and into another that seemed richer, finer, and much more desirable.

Between numbers he glanced shyly at Bess or Ted and exchanged a few whispered remarks. Fred had had to work this evening, Bess told him. And Mabel wasn't feeling well, Ted said. They'd both be sorry they had missed him.

When the concert ended and they were outside once more, Bess had another idea. "Let's go out to my house and raid the kitchen," she suggested. "I know there's cake. I baked it myself."

Suddenly a wave of shyness overwhelmed Jack. This was too much for one evening. He couldn't do it—go into this girl's house, a place he'd never seen, maybe meet her father and mother. Not yet, anyway.

"I—I'd better not," he stammered. "I've got to do some—studying tomorrow. Some writing," he went on lamely. "So I'd better get some sleep." He laughed nervously.

"Then we'll do it some other time," Bess said as they parted.

Jack turned away, disgusted with himself for making such a poor excuse. But then he forgot it as, all the way home, he reviewed and savored every moment of his incredible evening.

At five o'clock on Sunday, one week later, Jack leaned over the kitchen sink scrubbing his hands in a basin of soapy water. He lifted first one and then the other from the suds, examined the raw flesh, and scrubbed again with a short, stiff brush.

"Where's your scissors, Ma?" he asked.

His mother reached into a drawer, handed him the scissors, and watched him pare the rough, broken edges from his fingernails and dig under them with the point of a blade.

"That bricklaying job sure made my hands sore," he commented.

He dried his hands on the kitchen towel and examined the raw flesh again, frowning.

"Going somewhere?" she asked.

"Yeh," he answered as he disappeared into his room off the kitchen.

In a few minutes he returned in a new white shirt, a stiff collar in his hand.

"Hook this thing on for me, will you, Ma?"

He leaned over while she pushed the hook on the back of the neckband through the stiff buttonhole of the collar.

"Buying white shirts instead of food," she grumbled. "Want your supper now?"

"I'm not going to eat here tonight," he replied, grimacing as he pulled the stiff white circle around his neck. "Hey—fasten this thing, Ma, won't you? My hands are sore as blazes."

His mother reached up, jerked the offensive collar into place, and fastened it around her son's muscular neck. "Jack London," she snapped, "you mean you're spending good money to take a girl someplace for her supper? Seems to me—"

Jack pulled away and ran a finger under the edge of the collar where it bit into his flesh. "I'm not buying supper for anybody. I'm invited to go to somebody's house to eat."

He heard his mother gasp as he swung into his room and slammed the door. But in a few moments he emerged once more, necktie knotted tight around the collarband, coat on. His face was red and his lips tight as he stopped to run a wet comb through his hair before dashing out the door.

He snapped the clips around his trouser legs, jumped onto his wheel, and scorched out of the yard and down the street before any of the neighbors could comment. Already his shirt was wet from the exertion and he could feel little beads of sweat on his forehead and neck. But soon, as he pedaled along, the fresh late afternoon breeze cooled him and he calmed down.

He knew that he had been in a ferment of anxiety ever since Fred Jacobs had told him, on Friday night at the library, that he was invited to the Applegarths' for Sunday evening supper. A dozen times he had told himself that he wouldn't go. Even while he was buying the shirt and collar on Saturday night he was sure he'd have to make some excuse to Fred.

But this morning as he lay in bed, smelled the coffee boiling in the kitchen, and thought of another dreary meal at the kitchen table that night, he made up his mind. It wasn't enough to learn things from books. Words, for instance. You had to use them to be sure how they sounded. Already he'd learned some tricks from Fred Jacobs and Ted Applegarth, like shaking hands and saying "How do you do."

I've got a lot more to catch onto, he told himself, and I might as well start now—tonight—at the Applegarths'. Anyway, they want me to come, or they wouldn't have invited me for supper.

As Jack slowed down before the address that Fred had given him, and looked up at the big house that he was about to enter, he grimly remembered that he had been inside places like this before. He had washed windows in plenty of houses that were as good as this one. And a year before, he had battered the gates for meals at some that were even better.

He set his shoulders and walked resolutely up the steps and across the wide porch.

Ted greeted him warmly, took his cap, and led him into the big parlor. Fred and Bessie were already there, and before Jack had time to look around and get his bearings among a profusion of tables, lamps, chairs, books, paintings, and bric-a-brac, they had settled him into a deep, soft chair next to the grand piano and had drawn him into their conversation.

Why, coming here wasn't bad at all, he thought, as he tried to catch up with their conversation and glance around at the same time. What had he been so scared of?

Bess had some new pupils to tutor this summer, and

she was excited over the prospect of earning extra money for the night classes that she hoped to take. Jack looked at her, puzzled. She had nice clothes and didn't look like any of the working girls that he knew. Couldn't her folks send her to school?

"Bessie's a whiz at math," Fred explained proudly when he saw the puzzled look on Jack's face. "But her father thinks girls don't need to go to universities, so she's trying to manage by herself. She's good at English grammar, too," he added. "Knows every rule in the books."

Jack took another look, saw the fine, intelligent face, the hazel eyes with their long, thick lashes, and thought, with a twinge of envy, how lucky Fred was.

And then he heard a light, tinkling voice, and his spine froze with the advent of a new and terrifying unknown. Ted's sister, Mabel. He had forgotten about her. As Fred and Ted rose he grasped the arms of the chair and tried to pull himself up. On the second try he made it, and stood flushed and panting, his arms dangling at his sides, his throat dry.

"Mabel, this is Jack London," Ted said.

Jack looked, and all words left him. She was lovelier than her picture. Her hair, a pale gold cloud, seemed to illuminate her blue eyes and delicate oval face. Her soft dress billowed lightly about her as she drifted toward him.

With a start, Jack remembered. "How do you do," he murmured hoarsely.

130

She held out her hand and he took it. He could scarcely believe how small and soft it was as he heard her say, "I was so sorry to miss the concert last week. But now you've made us all very happy by coming to-night."

As she withdrew her hand, Jack felt his rough palm rasp against it. He wanted to apologize. He glanced at Fred, saw a merry twinkle in his eyes, and shoved his hand into his pocket.

"It was real nice of you to ask me, Miss," he answered. His voice sounded gruff, but she did not seem to notice.

In a few minutes Jack endured the ordeal of meeting her mother, a small, young-looking woman with a mass of shiny brown hair piled high on her head. She, too, seemed fragile compared with the women he had known, but there was a strength in her movements that her daughter did not have. He noticed the look of adoration on Mabel's face and was awed by it. Women he knew did not look at each other that way. His mother and Eliza —they got along all right, but neither one gave an inch in a scrap. This girl Mabel, he decided, would do what her mother said and not talk back.

Maybe that's the way it is in nice homes like this, he thought. And then he stole a glance at Bess and wasn't so sure. She seemed to have more fight in her.

Before Jack had time to think further, he and the others were following Mrs. Applegarth into the dining room, where a whole new set of problems confronted him in the form of sparkling glass and rows of silver. He

131

found himself in a chair between Mabel and her mother before he realized, with relief, that Mr. Applegarth wasn't going to be there. He was a mining engineer, Fred had told him, and was away from home much of the time.

Think I'd bolt if he came walking in, too, Jack told himself. Couldn't handle much more.

At first he was so busy watching what others were doing, trying not to let his fork clatter when he put it down, to chew quietly, and to get each mouthful down before he had to answer a question from Mrs. Applegarth or Mabel, that he couldn't hear what the others were saying. But gradually he began to relax. He was getting the hang of it, he realized with surprise. Just like handling the gear on the *Sophia Sutherland*. After a few times, it was easy.

The one thing that wasn't easy was getting used to glimpsing the pale, soft hands of the girl beside him or hearing her light voice clip off words so precisely. His own speech sounded rough and uncouth to him whenever he spoke, and he made up his mind to try to change it. Once his hand touched hers as he gestured in the middle of a sentence, and he stammered to a halt. Again he caught the twinkle in Fred's eyes across the table, and his face blazed. He ran a finger under the edge of his stiff collar and felt the raw flesh that it had cut.

After dinner Mabel played the piano, her delicate fingers displaying a strength and agility that astonished

Jack. While Ted and Fred played a game that they called chess, and Bess talked quietly with Mrs. Applegarth, Jack sat in a deep chair and feasted upon the sight and sound of beauty unknown to him before.

Later, as he rode his bicycle slowly toward East Oakland, he remembered vaguely that this was the night when he had intended to go to the meeting down on Washington Street that Jim Whitaker had told him about. But the problems of the world seemed remote and unimportant now. He pedaled his wheel for several blocks past his home before he could bring himself to turn around and go through the bare little kitchen to his room.

Chapter **9**

Now Jack began to live two distinctly different lives, and only in his thoughts did their paths cross. The life of work and study did not slacken. But always, now, as he rushed through the odd jobs that paid his way during this summer of 1895, or pedaled furiously from one place to another, his mind was filled with things so new to him that he could only wonder over them.

Picnics. Bicycle trips into the hills or across the bay by ferry. Sunday night suppers at the Madderns' or the Applegarths' followed by discussions of things they had all read. Only in books had he known such a life before!

It won't last, he sometimes told himself to cushion the disappointment that he was sure would come some day. They'll get tired of having a bum like me around.

But the fun went on, and by midsummer Jack began to lose his fear of being left out—his fear of not being able to see Mabel Applegarth any more. Vaguely he knew that he was in love with her. But she was so remote, so far above him. How could he ever hope to be worthy of her?

Each day he watched his speech and manners carefully and was pleased to hear himself begin to clip off his words as she did instead of running them all together, as did most of the people he knew. This was the way nice people talked, he decided, and he wanted to talk their way.

But sometimes when he forgot and used some of the phrases of his tramping and seafaring days, he was covered with mortification. What do they see in a rough fellow like me? he wondered.

At last, one evening, he believed he had the answer. Over a close game of chess with Ted Applegarth, he forgot himself again and let out a string of expletives that he thought he had discarded for good. Horrified, he looked up at Ted, expecting to see revulsion on his face.

Instead, there was a faraway look in Ted's eyes.

"You've been to so many interesting places and have done so many interesting things," he said.

Then Jack knew that Ted, in spite of his books and his sheltered way of life, secretly envied him. Ted was surrounded by women. But through Jack, he could catch glimpses of men living by brute strength and defying the forces of nature itself.

Gradually, when Jack understood, he began to entertain the group with stories about his experiences on the sea and the road. As his words rushed forth to draw vivid pictures of typhoons and smoking volcanoes and violence among men, he knew that he was repaying them for some of the lessons in etiquette and grammar and the subtleties of poetry. But a look of horror in Mabel's eyes always brought his stories to an end, and he could seldom be persuaded to tell another yarn for several days.

At the end of summer, the carefree excursions grew less frequent as the five friends went their separate ways: Ted and Mabel to the university, Fred to Anderson's Academy, and Bess to night school after a day of tutoring. Jack settled down to the old routine—janitor work, high school, study and writing.

Throughout the fall, the group met on Sunday nights as before, but talk was most often of school affairs, now, and Jack felt left out. What was interesting about the high school? Once it had been the goal of his life; but now, when he heard the others tell of their stimulating classes, their enthusiasm for their professors, a feeling of impatience and resentment came over him that left him restless and moody. The only good thing about the high school was the *Aegis* which was publishing one of his stories in nearly every issue during the fall. But he couldn't talk about that without seeming to brag.

One Sunday night, Jack started toward the Applegarths' as usual. It was a dreary night and he needed cheering up. His mother, in another of her irrational attempts to make a small fortune, had bought some lottery tickets again instead of paying the grocer, who was now demanding his money. In a stormy family scene, she had made the pointed remark that *somebody* had to bring in money in the family, and he had walked out.

Now he was in no mood to go to the Applegarths', where the sight of so much graciousness and comfort only intensified the difference between his home and theirs. And yet he couldn't go back home either.

As he neared the center of Oakland, an idea came to him. The Sunday night meetings that other Englishman, Whitaker, had invited him to—why not try one? There'd be talk and maybe some real action if some of the men got worked up the way they did in the street meetings.

"A good fight's what I need right now," he mumbled.

He hadn't really told Mabel he'd be coming to see her, though he knew she'd be expecting him. And there was an unfinished game of chess with Ted waiting on the table for his next move. But chess and music and poetry didn't suit his mood tonight.

With the quick, sure movement of a sailor changing his course, he turned toward Washington Street and started down it. His arms began to swing and the sailor's roll came into his stride. He pulled out his false teeth, dropped them into his pocket, and rubbed his tongue around his sore gums. Then he laughed and struck out at a fast clip.

Straight ahead a few blocks were rows of saloons

137

where, if he wanted to, he could find plenty of companionship among sailors from all over the world. But he shook his head and turned in at the building with the sign over it: SOCIALIST HALL.

In the upstairs room, men stood around in groups. The air was thick with smoke, but in a corner Jack sighted Jim Whitaker and headed toward him. He had seen the Englishman several times since their first conversation, and each time had promised to come to meetings. But on Sundays, the lure of pale gold hair and a soft voice had always been too strong until tonight.

Whitaker greeted him with a hearty handshake. "Well, London, so you've come at last," he said, his gaunt, rugged face breaking into a sly smile. "Thought that pretty girl I've seen you with would be too much competition for us."

Jack grinned. He liked this fellow Whitaker. There was something about him. . . . Life wasn't easy for him, Jack knew, but it hadn't broken him. He looked like a man who saw through things, knew what was wrong with the world, and was trying to do something about it.

In a few minutes Jack had shaken a dozen hands and was busy sizing up the crowd.

These weren't all working men, he could see. He knew that class. One was a minister, he learned. Another was a teacher in the university. Some talked like those fellows in Baltimore who had argued about economics and philosophy and had set him on fire to learn more.

This was a meeting of the Oakland section of the Socialist Labor party, Jack learned. He sat beside Jim Whitaker and listened to a discussion of street meetings. Chabot Park, behind the Oakland High School, was the one place where city officials sanctioned unauthorized public speaking. But the party members did not want to be limited to only that area. What about freedom of speech in America? Shouldn't they be permitted to speak wherever they liked without constant interference from the police?

The group came to no conclusions, but during the evening Jack heard some fiery speeches and was thrilled by them. He heard the words "class struggle" and understood them. He was of the class they were talking about, and he had struggled.

On the way out, Jim turned to him. "If you ever have the time and want to talk, come on over to the store. Maybe you don't know that the party saved me and my family from near starvation when I came here from Canada. They opened a cooperative grocery store in Alameda and put me in charge." He gave Jack the address and hurried off in the dark.

All the way home, the excitement of the evening stayed with Jack. Here was something to work for and here were men to work with. He didn't have much time to spare, but he should be able to do *something*.

And then the idea suddenly came to him to write an

article for the *Aegis*. Those middle class boys and girls in the high school needed shaking up. Educate the masses—that would be his theme. His fingers itched for a pencil as phrases raced through his head. Before he reached home he had decided on the title. "Optimism, Pessimism and Patriotism," he'd call it.

When the article appeared in the *Aegis* in December, however, it was not the students who were shaken up, but the teachers and the principal, Mr. McChesney. In the heat of his argument, Jack had accused the powers of withholding education from the masses in the fear that they would revolt against their long hours and low wages.

But he did not care any longer what they thought. The slow pace of learning in the high school was becoming unbearable. He knew that he could progress much faster than the other students, if only there was a way. Somehow he must find it!

At the beginning of the Christmas holiday, when Jack carried his books home, he knew that he would not return.

Mr. Bamford was Jack's chief source of comfort and encouragement during the early part of 1896. When Jack approached the desk, his face drawn and discouraged, the librarian always had cheerful words for him.

"Many men have gained eminence without a university education," he said repeatedly. "The books are here. You've begun to find your way among them."

But Jack was not satisfied. "I've learned some things, but there are so many gaps. Sometimes when I'm reading I think I haven't learned anything at all. Have to look up half the words in the dictionary and by the time I've learned what they mean I can't remember what I've read. What I need are whole courses in things like philosophy and literature. Not just the high school stuff, but real stuff that goes deep so that I can get all of it."

Mr. Bamford shook his head. "You're reaching for the stars, my boy," he said kindly. "You want to cram a whole lifetime of learning into a few years."

Jack's troubled eyes took on a determined look and he clenched his fists. "That's it. That's what I've been trying to say. I want to reach out and take hold of the stars. Get 'em in my hands. And some day I'm going to do it."

But now even reading frustrated him, for he had no immediate goal. He was sure that he wanted to be a writer, but he didn't know where to begin. For hours he thumbed through magazines in the library and saw things in print that he was sure weren't as good as the stories he had written for the *Aegis*. Then he spent days shut in his room trying to get some of his thoughts onto paper, only to give up in disgust.

One evening he found Fred and Ted at the Applegarths' studying for their next day's classes, and the sight of them brought his resentment and frustration to the boiling point. Why should they be privileged to have what he was denied? His brains were as good as theirs —better, maybe.

He slumped down into a chair, his face black with despair.

"How can I do it?" he cried. "I've *got* to get into the university somehow. You fellows don't realize—I don't have much time left." How could he explain to them what it was like to live off his father's meager pension and earnings and watch his mother's face grow more grim each day? He couldn't.

Fred pulled off his glasses and rubbed his tired eyes. "I know how you feel, Jack. When I was working in the library and going to night school, sometimes I thought I couldn't stand the slow pace. Then I asked some questions and got some answers. There are only two ways to get into the university if you don't finish high school. You have to pass entrance examinations, and they're stiff—history, literature, math, chemistry, physics. . . . Without a laboratory it's just about impossible to learn the sciences.

"Or there's the other way—a cramming school like Anderson's. But it's expensive, you know that."

Jack knew. He had even thought of going back to the despised mills to try to earn the money. But it would take years to save enough, and meanwhile he would be expected to help out more at home. Twice he had started out for Johnny Heinold's—the First and Last Chance saloon—with the idea of asking for a loan. But he needed too much. Johnny would give him the money, he knew, but how long would it be before he could return it?

There was always Eliza. She had helped him before. Now, when he had just passed twenty, he knew he shouldn't ask her again. But he was desperate. If he could only have an education he was sure that he could pay her back many times over.

Color began to rise in Jack's face as the possibility grew in his mind.

"How does it work, Fred—at the cramming joint? How do they get you to the university faster than the high school does?"

"You take the work in units," Fred explained. "Whatever you haven't taken in high school. If you can pass the required number of units at Anderson's you don't have to take the entrance examinations."

"You mean you can go as fast as you want to?"

"As fast as you *can*. Some of the fellows take years, or don't make it at all. It's not easy!" He sighed, put on his glasses, and turned back to his book.

Slowly Jack pulled himself from his chair and wandered out the door, forgetting to say good-by. As fast as he wanted to! Why, he'd go so fast he'd leave everybody behind! Literature . . . chemistry . . . physics. . . . He ticked them off in his mind one after the other.

And then he jumped onto his bicycle and raced across town toward Eliza's. She had never failed him. She wouldn't fail him now!

A few days later Jack emerged from Anderson's Academy in Alameda, his face radiant, his eyes glowing. "By golly, I did it," he cried. Passersby stared and smiled at the big-shouldered boy in the flappy clothes standing alone in the wind on the steps of the Academy and radiating his happiness to the world.

He let out a whoop and raced down the steps to the bicycle stand. He had done it—paid Eliza's money to Mr. Anderson and signed up for the spring term that would start in March. Meanwhile, he'd begin his assault on the books!

As he wheeled his bicycle into the street, he wanted to tell somebody—anybody—about it. But Ted and Mabel were six miles away in Berkeley at the university. And Bess was teaching her pupils. He had caught a glimpse of Fred in a small laboratory when Mr. Anderson had shown him the school.

He hesitated, and then he remembered Jim Whitaker's grocery store. "Come in anytime you want to talk," he had said.

Jack found the store down near the wharf. As he entered the old building he noticed that there were no displays of fancy goods. This was a workingman's store, stocked with the things that workmen's families could buy. He noted the open barrels of flour, red Mexican beans, and oatmeal; bags of cheap tobacco in a case on the counter.

The sound of ripping boards led him to the back of the store where Whitaker was prying the lid from a packing case. His sleeves were rolled above the elbows and the well-developed muscles of the Englishman's arms surprised Jack.

Jim Whitaker looked up, smiled, and laid down his hammer. "You look as though you'd just robbed a bank and got away with it," he said. "Glad to see you. Come on. This can wait." He led the way to the front of the store and pulled up two empty cracker barrels for seats.

"Well, out with it. What have you done?"

"I've just enrolled in Anderson's Academy for the spring term."

Jim stared and then whistled softly. "You did rob a bank! Moving in with the rich fellows now, eh?"

Jack looked at him startled, and then he flushed.

"Never thought about it that way," he said honestly. "I've got to get into the university in a hurry, and this is the quickest way. My sister let me have the money. I figure I can pay her back and then some if I can just finish up my education."

Jim was silent for a moment. "A university degree is a fine thing to have," he said, "if you don't . . ." He hesitated.

"If I don't what?"

"If you don't let it become more important than what you learn."

Jack nodded. He wasn't exactly sure what Jim Whitaker was driving at, but if he thought— "I've got a lot of things to learn," he rushed on. "Literature and history. And the natural sciences. I want to know all about the—the cosmos, I think that's the word, and . . ." His voice dwindled off as he wondered if he should take this man into his confidence. Maybe he would laugh and try to talk him out of it.

"You see, I've decided I want to be a writer. I've got the feel for it," he plunged on. "I've written a lot of stuff and I like to do it. Sometimes I sit up all night writing and never know the difference. Only, a writer has to know just about everything, it seems to me. And I aim to fill up my head as fast as I can."

He watched his companion's face, and with a start heard him murmur, "A whole lifetime of learning in a few years, eh?" Mr. Bamford had said that, too.

"Yeh. You see, I haven't got much time."

Suddenly Jim slapped a hand down on Jack's knee, and he winced. That fellow's stronger than he looks, he thought, as he watched him go behind the counter and bring out a thick sheaf of manuscript pages.

"Go to it, Jack," he said. "I envy you." And then he riffled through the pages in his hands, a wry little smile on his lean face. "When I first saw you in City Hall Park I never dreamed that I'd be making confessions to you. I, too, have the dream."

Jack stared and then looked around the store. In its way, it was almost as grim as the jute mill, though here were no foremen looking over Jim's shoulder.

"Why don't you write, then? Chuck this and go after it."

Jim shrugged. "I have a wife and seven children," he said, as he pushed the pages back into the drawer.

Until the spring term opened, Jack came often to the store, pedaling his bicycle down through the area he had known so intimately as a boy, the half of Oakland that the people of the other half scarcely knew existed, the area of wharves and shanties and saloons and sailors' boarding houses. Sometimes an artist came down to paint pictures of the "characters" and the shanties in which they lived. Or families of means drove quickly through in their carriages on their way to the yacht clubs. Or commuters to San Francisco rode the streetcars to the ferry terminal, intent upon their newspapers. Otherwise, for them it did not exist.

But Jack, wheeling back and forth, saw it again as he had seen it in his boyhood, when his innocent country-boy eyes saw too much, too young. As he crossed the Webster Street Bridge that spanned the estuary and linked Oakland with Alameda, he recalled the brutal fights of the street gangs that he had later taken up with, when they had chosen the bridge as their battlefield because it offered an escape at either end if the police moved in.

Sometimes he thought, as he rode along remembering all he had been and done, that his life had been made up of sections or layers, each one completely different, and each sloughed off as the next emerged. Now the student in him was trying to emerge. What next?

In Jim Whitaker, for the first time, he found a man with whom he could discuss his past and his future. Jim, too, had some experiences to talk about. In the British army he had been an instructor in athletics and gymnastics. In Canada he had tried farming on a grand scale and had been defeated. And they had a common goal—they both wanted to write about their experiences.

But as soon as the spring term started at Anderson's, the leisurely hours with Jim came to an end. For Jack had made up his mind. Shattering all precedents, he would slash through the required work in one term and enter the university in the fall.

Chapter **10**

Five weeks after Jack entered Anderson's Academy, fired with determination to conquer the books as no one had before, he parked his bicycle at Eliza's one morning and tramped up the back steps to the open kitchen door.

Eliza looked up from her ironing in surprise. "Why, Jack," she said. "What are you doing here? Why aren't you in school?" Then her surprise changed to apprehension when she saw her brother's face, drained of its color. His eyes were dull; his big shoulders sagged as he dropped into a chair and laid his head on his arms.

"You're sick!" she cried. "I knew all that studying day and night would get you down. Nobody can stand it, I told you, Jack." She ran a hand over his forehead. "Thank goodness you don't seem to have a fever. You're just beat out, that's all. Now you come on and I'll get you to bed."

She tugged at him but he shook her off. "Beat out," he mumbled. "That's it, I'm beat out."

As though with great effort he raised his head, reached into his pocket, and brought out a handful of gold coins, spilling them across the table. "There it is, Eliza. There's your money, every dollar of it. Mr. Anderson gave it all back. Real polite about it, too. Said he was sorry."

Eliza sat down across the table from her brother and slowly arranged the coins into neat stacks.

"Some things you just can't fight, Jack," she said at last. "You're trying too hard, reaching too fast. You're smart enough, but those boys at Anderson's have had advantages all their lives. You mustn't feel bad about not being able to keep up with them."

"Keep up with 'em!" All the hurt and resentment and anger of the past hour flared out from Jack's tired, bloodshot eyes. He banged the table with his clenched fists. "Keep up with *them?*" he raged. "Why, I passed 'em up, that's what I did. Passed right by every one of 'em. There wasn't a one that could keep up with *me*. And so they got sore. Went in and complained to Mr. Anderson. Their folks complained, too. Said the school would get a bad name letting a fellow get through two years of high school in one term."

He shoved back his chair sending it crashing against the wall as he slammed to his feet. He stamped up and down the kitchen, banged a kettle onto the stove, drove a clenched fist against his palm.

"What's a cramming joint for? That's what I asked him. I crammed, that's what I did, and they didn't like it. He kept saying he was sorry. Real polite. He *was* sorry, too, I guess. But he said he had the school to think of. Couldn't get in bad with the university."

At last when he had worn out his storm, Jack slumped back into the chair, his face as bleak as before.

"What are you going to do now," Eliza asked meekly. "Get a job?"

There it was again—that question. Get a job? Get a job? He'd heard it a thousand times. Even heard it in his sleep.

Eliza watched his jaw set and the old fighting spirit come back into his eyes.

"No. I'm going to get ready for those examinations in August. I've got twelve weeks left, and I've learned how to cram. I'm going to pass those examinations."

"Good," Eliza murmured. "I didn't think you'd give up." She clinked the gold coins that lay on the table and then shoved one toward him. "You'll need some books and things. No odd jobs, now. You won't have time. Tell Ma I'll help out at home till August."

As Jack left Eliza's, he began to plan his attack on the books. If he could pass the examinations in just four subjects, English, history, mathematics, and physics, he could enter the university as a special student. This he knew. The degree could go hang; he'd figure out how to get that later.

At home he explained in a few words what had happened and gave his mother the message from Eliza. And

151

then he went into his little room and closed the door. First he gathered together all the stories and essays that he had written and put them away in a bureau drawer. Then he threw everything else from his table onto the bed and set up his office: text books, paper, pencils, notes from his uncompleted units at Anderson's. He made out a list of books that he would need from the library.

And last, from the bed he picked up the reading list that the Socialist Labor party had put out that year: Bellamy, Sothern, Jones . . . He had planned to read all of them so that he could hold his own in arguments at the meetings. But they, too, would have to wait. He stacked up all the remaining books that he had brought home from the library and went out.

As he rode his bicycle west toward the library, he looked around regretfully. It was a beautiful day in late April. Flowers bloomed by every doorway. Far to his right, on the hillsides, great splashes of golden poppies and purple lupine flashed in the sun. And to his left, down at the water's edge, his little skiff lay waiting to carry him out for a day of fishing or roaming through the estuary and out into the harbor.

Picnics, bicycle trips, boating—all would have to go on without him. Until August, nothing must interfere with his plan. Five hours of sleep at night would be all that he would allow himself, he decided. If he got stuck in physics and math, Fred and Bess would help him, he knew. And Mabel would understand and admire his ambition, he believed. In a sense, even though she didn't know it, wasn't he doing this for her, to make himself worthy of her? And yet there was something else inside him that drove him on.

Off to the left, smoke rose from the mills and factories of Oakland, and in those grim buildings stood boys and girls at the machines, their faces sallow, their backs bent. Maybe it's fear that drives me, he told himself. Fear of having to go back to the mills. I don't know. But whatever it is, I'm going to pass those examinations!

As he parked his bicycle at the library and started up the steps, all his bewilderment and resentment brought him to one final resolution. He'd go down to the meeting on Sunday night and sign up as a member of the Socialist Labor party.

On August 12, 1896, Jack shuffled out of the Mechanics Building on the University of California campus and stood blinking into the sunlight. He started to raise his hand to shield his eyes, found his pen still clutched in his fingers, and idly wiped it on his trousers and fumbled for his pocket. His hand and arm were numb, and he stood in a kind of dumb stupor, rubbing his fingers and arm, until someone jostled him. Then slowly he moved down the steps and onto the path that led south. His knees quivered strangely and every muscle in his body ached as though he had been shoveling coal.

The examinations were over. For three days he had sat in that building answering question after question, working quadratic equations, identifying and explaining poems. And for three nights he had scarcely slept while he reviewed and crammed for the next day.

Now it was over. He looked around at the drying grass and up at the brown hills. Summer was almost over, too. He hadn't seen anyone for weeks except Fred and Bess once in a while when he needed help. Vaguely he remembered that he had gone to the Applegarths' one Sunday night and had snored in a chair while Mabel played for him.

Now he was free. After three months a prisoner in his room, he was free. But there was no elation in the thought. He had been keyed up too long.

At the south gate of the campus, Jack pulled his stiff body up the steps of a streetcar and slumped into a seat.

"Whew," he breathed.

All the way down Telegraph Avenue he dozed, his mind blank. When he reached Oakland, he automatically transferred to a Fourteenth Street car and continued toward home. Now and then the thought came to him that he should tell his friends about the examinations. Mr. Bamford would want to know. And Fred, who was working in the library during the summer, would be eager to hear. But the library had books in it, and he didn't want even to see a book. Besides, he wouldn't know the results of the examinations for a week, and now he couldn't remember a single answer he had written.

As Jack stumbled up his own front steps, he steeled himself for questions. But the house was empty. He wandered into his room, and the sight of it revolted him. He looked at his bed. He was nearly dead for sleep, but he couldn't sleep in that bed, that room, that prison!

Where Jack's mind refused to function, his instinct took charge. He found himself rolling the blankets from his bed and scrambling through the pantry for food. His feet carried him out the door and down toward the bay, while his sailor's instinct told him to leave his little skiff behind and borrow a small sailboat from a waterfront acquaintance.

That night he slept on the boat, and in the early morning drifted out of the estuary with the tide. Behind him was everything that he wanted to forget. Ahead lay adventure, the old adventure of sea and tide and wind.

As the tide turned and a spanking breeze hit his sail, he raced along into San Pablo Bay. All the old landmarks that he knew from his wild carefree days on the bay sprang up before him, and he passed them one by one, reveling in the sight of them and the feel of the tiller tugging at his arm. Spray and sun bit into his sallow cheeks, and the taste of salt on his lips was delicious.

He rounded the Solano wharf and surged on toward

Benicia. Here for a while when he was sixteen, as a member of the fish patrol, he had lain in his sloop waiting to pounce upon fishermen in the act of setting their illegal nets. What a time he had had!

Four years ago, he thought, but maybe some of the old crowd are still around.

As he passed the tules and skimmed close to the shore, he scanned the cluster of old boats for a familiar one. On a sudden impulse he sailed on in, made fast his sailboat, and wandered around the wharf.

"Jack! Jack London! Why, you old salt—where have you come from?"

It was Charley Le Grant, head of the fish patrol. He threw his arms around Jack and then pulled him along.

"Lizzie!" he cried. "Look who's here. Jack London."

From a cabin, Lizzie Le Grant emerged, her round, weathered face crinkling with delight. She smothered him in a warm embrace as others came running up. Bill Murphy—Joe Lloyd—fishermen of all nationalities who remembered him. They shouted and he shouted. A celebration was under way before he knew what was happening. There were drink and talk as the day moved on, with never a thought for the passing of time. They retold every yarn of the old days when Jack was one of them, and they begged him to stay on with them.

But as the tide turned and he looked out at the white-capped water and heard the howl of a rising wind, he wanted to be out in it, even in the little borrowed sail-boat.

Charley Le Grant, however, taking stock of the fierce ebb and wild wind, slipped out to the wharf and transferred Jack's blankets and small stock of food to a larger Columbia River salmon boat that could sail in any wind. He added supplies of meat and coffee and a fisherman's charcoal brazier and at the last put in a freshly caught black bass.

As Jack cast off and waved good-by to the crowd on the wharf, the years seemed to melt away. He set his sail and drove into the wind, singing all the old sea chanteys that he had not sung in four long years.

For a week, Jack sailed from one end of the great bay to the other while his mind and body recuperated. Many times he could have reveled with old friends at familiar wharves, but he avoided them. Let the sun and wind and long hours of sleep in sheltered coves do their work. He needed nothing more.

At the end of the week, sunbrowned and at peace, he returned home eager to learn the results of his examinations. A letter on his table contained the news. He had passed and could enter the university in September as a special student.

The University of California! As Jack strode toward the steps of North Hall and looked up at the ivy-covered walls, his thoughts flew back to that day two years before when he, a tramp, one of the lowliest members of society, had made up his mind to climb out of the pit and into the sunshine. Education was the ladder on which he would climb. And here he was, incredibly, walking into North Hall to register for his first semester.

He glanced around. Fred was somewhere in the crowd of students, no doubt, and Ted, too, though he was a sophomore. Jack saw familiar faces, some of his old schoolmates from Cole School, grown up now so that he could hardly recognize them.

They probably won't remember me, he thought, but I don't care.

Some of the fellows from Anderson's were familiar enough. He smiled wryly and tried to imagine their surprise if they recognized him in the crowd of freshmen.

I showed 'em, he exulted. They thought they could stop me.

As he walked up the steps he pulled from his pocket the creased and pencil-marked booklet that announced the courses from which he could choose, and his face glowed with anticipation of all that he could learn here. But then he frowned as he looked them over again. Why would the university allow him only five courses? He wanted to take a dozen.

The question of which courses Jack should take had filled long evenings at the Applegarths'. For Fred, the decision was easy. He wanted to be a chemist. But a writer had to know just about everything. Mabel wanted him to take History of English Literature, and he had definitely decided upon that one. Soon he would be able to hold his own in the Sunday night discussions. Bess thought that mathematics would be fine discipline for his mind. He was sure she was right, but he reluctantly crossed off First Year Mathematics in favor of two courses in composition. Two courses covering the political history of the Middle Ages and the Nineteenth Century would give him background for talk at the party meetings and for some writing that he already had in mind to do.

Jack tucked his open-necked shirt more firmly into his flappy trousers and took a place in the line of students. That he, too, was not dressed in the latest attire for college students did not concern him. His mind was on much more important matters.

Yes, those five courses along with odd jobs and writing ought to keep me busy, he decided. And if I have time left over, there's a whole list of books that I haven't got into, waiting at the library.

For a while, Jack's enthusiasm remained at a high pitch. He opened his mind for the knowledge that was to pour into it from lectures by learned professors, and he read far beyond the assignments. With his friends, he talked as excitedly as they about the things he was learning.

And yet, as the weeks went on, doubts began to torment him, especially when he squirmed through an interminable hour listening to a professor expound a point that he had understood in a few minutes. A waste of time, that's what it was.

Slowly the truth dawned upon him. There was nothing

he could learn here in the university that he couldn't get by himself from books. Only, he could go faster by himself. Mr. Bamford had been right. The books were there in the library, and already he knew how to find his way among them.

Stubbornly he clung on, however, while the forty dollars that he had borrowed from Johnny Heinold dwindled. And then one day, soon after he had registered for the second semester, he gave up. It wasn't worth it—all this running out to Berkeley and back again, this worry about money and his father's health. In five months he was no closer to his goal. He hadn't written a thing worth publishing except a few letters to editors of the local papers.

While he still had a little money left, before he was forced to get a job to support his mother and father and pay his debt to Johnny, there was only one thing to do —leave the university and write!

On February 4, 1897, Jack asked for and received his honorable dismissal from the University of California.

Chapter **11**

Ted Applegarth and Fred Jacobs listened patiently while Jack tried to explain what had happened to his glorious plans. But the swift change that five months in the university had made in Jack's outlook was more than either of them could grasp.

"You didn't give the university a chance, Jack," Fred said. "I'm getting what I want. Maybe you should have gone into science. It's the coming thing. There's a great future in it."

Jack laughed sardonically. "Science. Electricity. When I was eighteen, somebody else told me that. His name was Mr. Grimm and he was superintendent of the power plant of the Oakland Street Railway."

But he did not explain. It was impossible for either of these fellows with their soft muscles and sheltered backgrounds to understand what had happened to him out at the power plant.

Mabel Applegarth's reaction was the hardest for Jack

to bear, however. In the year and a half since he had met her, he had done everything possible to better himself in her eyes. He had watched his manners, improved his language, and read everything she had suggested. And he had seen her interest in him grow steadily, he was sure. Sometimes he caught a look in her eyes that was unmistakable. She was older than he, he knew. Did she want to wait forever?

He sat in a chair opposite her, red-faced and miserable. He could tell her none of these thoughts that kept prodding him to hurry—hurry—before someone else more eligible came into her life.

"Don't you see?" he pleaded. "By quitting the university and starting my writing at once, I'm saving three years. I've been studying the magazines. Do you know they pay two cents a word? Why, if I write only a thousand words a day—let's see—that's six hundred dollars a month! Don't you get what I'm driving at?"

But her blue eyes were cold with disapproval.

"You are much too concerned with money," she answered, clipping off each word as if to remind him that in his agitation he had slipped back into his slovenly way of speaking. "You need the discipline of a university education before you will be prepared to write. You are much too impatient, Jack."

Discipline! Blood rose to his hairline, and he felt his fingers curl into the old battling fist. Then he relaxed and drew a long sigh. It was no use. She couldn't understand. How could she? He would just have to go ahead and show her.

He declined an invitation to remain for supper and headed off toward Washington Street. Down in the old meeting room were plenty of men who hadn't gone through the discipline of a university.

Jack sought out Jim Whitaker at once.

"I've quit the university," he blurted out.

Jim smiled and looked him over. "Well, you don't seem to be taking it very hard. How do you feel about it?"

Jack grinned. "Matter of fact, I'm relieved," he said. "Maybe there's something wrong with me, but I got tired of all that kiddish stuff, football and class rivalry. Couldn't see what it was all for, at a university. And in the lectures, the professors kept talking about the past as though they didn't know a thing about what's going on now. It's all dead stuff."

Jim listened solemnly.

"How old are you, Jack?"

"Twenty-one."

"Maybe that's your problem. You *are* older. How much thinking were you doing when you were eighteen?"

Jack stared at him. Eighteen. At eighteen he was shoveling coal in the power plant, tramping across the country, learning about life in a penitentiary.

"At eighteen I was just beginning to think," he admitted.

"Well, come on and get in on the scrap tonight. We'll give you something to think about, and it won't be the past, either. It'll be what's happening in Oakland right now." He pulled Jack along to the front row and sat down beside him.

"What's it about?" Jack whispered.

"Ordinance 1676 again. The men want to make a test case."

Ordinance 1676. That same old law they were arguing about on his first visit to this hall. Jack went over it in his mind. No one was allowed to speak at a public meeting on any public street within the city limits without written permission from the mayor. Every now and then, at meetings, the subject came up.

The president called the meeting to order. "Now, men, there's been a lot of talk about Ordinance 1676," he said, "but we've never done anything about it. February twelfth is Lincoln's birthday. It's a holiday and there'll be people on the streets with time to stop and listen. We'll have to make a real soapbox case of this. Get out where the police are thickest, in the center of town. We'll never know if they can make this law stick until we get an arrest and a trial."

"That's right!" someone shouted, and the rest took up the cry.

"Quiet. Quiet, now. We've got to work this out. Who'll volunteer to do the speaking."

In a flash Jack was on his feet. "I'll do it," he said.

"That's the spirit," someone cried. "Jack London's the fellow."

Before he knew what was happening, Jack was surrounded by the other members who patted him on the back and shook his hand.

When the meeting finally broke up and Jack left with Whitaker, he began to realize what was ahead of him. Arrest. Maybe a jail sentence. He wasn't afraid, but one thing bothered him.

"Jim," he said. "I—I've never made a speech on the street. Don't know if I can do it. Come along with me, will you?"

"Sure. I'll even bring the soapbox. If you want to back out, though, I'll do it for you."

Jack shook his head. This was a free country and he believed in freedom of speech. Once it had been denied him in Buffalo, and he had spent a month in prison. But here things would be different. They'd win their case, and he wanted to help them do it.

But when Jack reached home, the everyday problems confronted him, and for several days he put aside all thought of the speech he must make while he threw himself pell-mell into the business of writing. If he could only sell something—anything—before his last cent was gone he might put off a little longer the day when he must go out looking for work. He wrote short stories and long essays. He wrote poems, long and short. All day he sat at his ink-splotched table in a fever of writing, sometimes refusing to stop in order to eat. But on Lincoln's birthday he broke away just in time to meet Jim Whitaker as he had promised.

Whitaker was already standing on the corner of Broadway and Fourteenth, soapbox in hand, when Jack ran up, out of breath.

"Thought you'd changed your mind," he said.

"No. Been working. Jim, if they put me in jail, see that I get some paper and pencils, will you? I can't waste the time."

Jim laughed and set the soapbox on the busy corner. "Don't worry. All your friends will be down to see you. Seriously, though, we don't think they can make the law stick. But you can still back out."

Jack shook his head. He wanted to go through with it—get it over as fast as possible so that he could go back to the story that he had left unfinished. But when he stepped up onto the box and people turned to stare, suddenly he was tongue-tied.

"What'll I say, Jim?" he whispered hoarsely.

"Oh, just anything, but make it loud."

Jack took a deep breath and felt his knees begin to shake. I should have practiced, he thought frantically.

"Go on, Jack!" Jim prompted him. "Say something!"

Jack opened his mouth as a crowd began to gather. "On this birthday of Abraham Lincoln, one of the greatest men—" he began. To his horror, his voice had come out thin and tremulous—high, like a girl's.

Someone laughed, and others joined him. "What's that you're saying, Sonny?" he heard.

The crowd began to walk away and Jim suddenly shoved Jack from the box and leaped up in his place. His voice rang out over the heads of passersby while Jack wiped the perspiration from his face and gathered his wits. More people were stopping to listen when suddenly a voice shouted, "Here come the cops!"

With a quick jerk, Jack pulled his friend from the box and leaped onto it. Now his voice came clear and strong as he threw out the words. "Freedom of speech . . . the constitution . . . inalienable rights" all jumbled together while he kept an eager eye on the oncoming police who would get him out of this misery.

"Here, you. Come along," he heard.

As he moved off between two policemen, he waved good-by to Jim, who was picking up the soapbox.

The next day, Jack, chagrined and angry, was back at his old table trying to finish his story while all of Oakland read his name in the headlines. The judge had treated him like a small boy, scolded him, and sent him home. He had gained nothing but notoriety. "Boy Socialist" the papers called him, while the law remained uncontested.

Now he cut himself off from everyone while he threw himself into his writing with even greater fury. From his brother-in-law, Captain Shepard, he borrowed an ancient, balky typewriter, and as he finished each piece he set himself to typing it. The keys were stiff and rusty, the letters were all capitals, and Jack had never typed before. He searched for a letter, hammered it with all his might, and then searched for the next one. His arms and shoulders began to ache and his mother complained over the racket he was making, but he typed on. He sold his schoolbooks and bought stamps, affixed them to envelopes, and sent his outpouring to magazines in the East. When he ran out of things to sell, the manuscripts stacked up on his table. Still he wrote.

And then, one by one, his stories and poems began to come back. In a few weeks, they had all been returned. Every one.

When the postman handed him the last envelope, Jack went back into his room, closed the door, and calmly read all of the rejected manuscripts through. Then he laid his tired head on his arms.

They aren't good enough, he told himself. I'll have to go slower, think things through, study more. Trouble is, I'm trying to write like other people instead of like myself.

To his mind came the first story that he had ever written, the story of the typhoon. He hadn't tried to copy anyone when he wrote that. Onto the paper he had poured his experience, just as he had thrilled to it on that wild day and night off the coast of Japan.

Out in the kitchen he heard the piping voice of a little

boy whom his mother was tending for a small fee while the child's mother worked. From his parents' bedroom he heard the rasping cough of his father, too weak and ill to work now.

Jack stacked the manuscripts neatly on his table and walked through the kitchen where his mother's harassed face reproved him. In the bedroom his father lay propped on pillows, his cheeks flushed with fever.

"It's just this old lung of mine," he whispered. "I'll be up again in a day or two. How's the writing, Johnny?"

"Fine. Just fine, Pa," Jack answered. "I can do it nights, now that I've got the hang of it. I'm going out to look for work."

By late afternoon on the following Sunday, Jack was far below San Francisco, wheeling along at a steady pace toward Belmont, a place that he had heard of but never seen. On his left was the southern part of San Francisco Bay; on his right over the ridge lay the ocean. He was hot and dusty, but the March sun on his back felt good after so many days spent indoors.

A job had been harder to find than even he had realized. But after standing in line at one employment office after another, he had had some luck. Belmont Academy, a select preparatory school, needed a helper for the laundry, and there were no experienced laundrymen available. Had he had experience? the agency man asked. Of course he had. His imagination and the urgent need for a job stretched into years of experience the washing he had done on shipboard and in rivers and creeks when he was tramping. The man took a look at his broad shoulders and said, "You'll do." It was as easy as that. No questions. No references.

As Jack wheeled into the little valley lush with grass and spring flowers, he began to think that this was the best thing that could have happened to him. His trunk full of the books that he had borrowed from everyone he knew was on its way. After work and on Saturday afternoons and Sundays, he could lie out in the grass and read.

The only jarring note in the picture was the pay— thirty dollars a month again. For all his reading and education, he was worth no more in the labor market. But board and room were free. He could send money home each month and keep a little for himself. Maybe he could save enough to carry him through a few more weeks of writing when the school closed for the summer.

Jack whistled cheerfully as he coasted down the last incline toward the school nestled in a little parklike valley surrounded by gently rolling hills.

Looks like a mansion, he thought. A place for rich kids.

He wheeled around toward the rear and parked his bicycle against a building noisy with the sound of clattering machines. A cloud of steam billowed from an open vent.

He knocked on the door and then stepped inside. Under the glare of electric lights a man, stripped to his undershirt, bent over a tub of steaming water. He looked up, swept the suds from his glistening arms, and surveyed Jack.

"You the new hand?" he asked.

Jack nodded.

"Well, you look strong enough. The last fellow gave out in a week. Come on in. Supper's about ready, and then I'll show you around. What's your name?"

"Jack."

"Mine's Joe."

In a few minutes, Joe led him across the yard to the school kitchen where a table was set for the help. He took his place with the gardeners and stable hands and listened to Joe complain about the long hours, the heat, and the pile of laundry that was never done. He looked at the other's thin, wiry arms and smiled to himself. Joe didn't look fit, but he, with his muscles, could stand up to the work, he was sure. Joe, obviously, had never hauled tackle on a ship or shoveled coal.

Afterward Joe showed him his room, a small one over the laundry. But there was a table in it, and his trunk, full of books, had already arrived. Afterward they went down to the laundry where Joe explained how the new, modern machinery worked.

Jack looked on admiringly. "It's a beauty, isn't it? Does just about everything."

171

Joe snorted. "Just about everything a *machine* can do. But there's plenty it can't do. You'll see. Ought to have three men for all the work they throw at me. I keep sayin' I'll quit. Maybe I will, too, someday."

As soon as he could get away, Jack went back up to his room. He was tired from the long ride, but before he went to bed he unpacked his books and arranged them on his table according to their classifications: philosophy, political economy, history, biology, literature, light fiction. Something here for every mood.

At night I'll start on the harder stuff, he decided. And I'll end with the poetry. Why, in a setup like this, I could even write!

The next morning at six-fifteen, a rap sounded on Jack's door, and at once he jumped out of bed, ready for the day. Breakfast over, he followed Joe into the laundry.

"You sort," Joe said, "while I get the washer goin' and mix up the soft soap. Shirts here, socks there, underwear . . . Get it?"

Jack nodded. This was easy. Nothing to it. He wondered why Joe was rushing around so fast.

"Gotta save every minute," he shouted over the noise of the machine.

The sorting finished, Jack dumped steaming clothes from the washer into the spinner and then shook them out for the dryer. Back and forth he went, meanwhile assisting Joe with the socks. All afternoon they ironed socks and underwear. Jack astonished Joe with his skill with the irons, but by supper time they were far from through.

"Gotta work after supper," Joe moaned. "Shirts tomorrow. Table linen and sheets Wednesday."

They toiled on until ten o'clock when the last sock and piece of underwear was folded and ready to go back to its owner. Jack stumbled upstairs to his room and turned on the light. Fourteen hours! He had already lost three or hour hours of reading time. Well, he'd got along on five hours of sleep before and he could do it again, he resolved. He pulled off his shoes and socks and settled himself on the bed with a book on political economy.

Sometime in the night Jack wakened, stiff and sore, a cool breeze blowing across his damp body. The book was still in his hand, his finger at page one. Painfully he pulled off his clothes, switched off the light, and got into bed.

The next day was worse. They washed, starched, and ironed shirts, again working until long after supper. That night Jack sat in a straight chair when he opened his book. He read two pages and then read them again while his eyelids drooped and his head nodded. He tried propping open his eyes with his fingers and pacing up and down the room to keep awake. But nothing worked. At last, in disgust, he pulled off his clothes and fell into bed.

So it went all week. At supper time the work was never done and the two men toiled on into the night. Jack did not even try to read. He fell into exhausted sleep as soon as he reached his room and in the morning he arose feeling as though he had been drugged.

On Saturday they finished at three o'clock. Jack lay on his bed all afternoon, too tired to sleep. Sunday he lay in the grass under a tree and tried to read the newspaper, but he did not finish it. The problems of the world no longer interested him. After supper he went to bed again.

The next week was the same. And the next. They put mountains of clothes through the cycle of washing, drying, ironing, only to be confronted by other mountains. As summer neared and the boys put on white duck trousers, the labor increased.

Jack drank gallons of water that seemed to run out of his pores as fast as he consumed it. Through the steam in which he seemed to be permanently engulfed, his dull mind tried at times to figure out what was happening to him. He had worked harder, he knew, when he was shoveling coal. But then, when he was eighteen, his mind was still asleep. Now that it was awake and eager, when his room was full of books that he wanted to read, his dulled body and spirit would not let him read them. He was a work beast again, no better off than he had been three years before.

At last when the school closed, Jack packed his books

and sent them back to Oakland. He had not read even one. Then he drew his last month's pay and wearily turned his wheel toward home. In his pocket was enough money to tide him over a few weeks of writing before he must look for another job. Only a miracle could save him from making the rounds of employment offices again, and he did not believe in miracles.

Chapter 12

Only a few weeks later, on the fifteenth of July, 1897, a stubby old steamer moved slowly into San Francisco Harbor. The faded letters on her rusty, smoke-grimed hull told that she was the *Excelsior,* a freighter that plied the waters between San Francisco and the little port of St. Michael beyond the muddy delta of the Yukon River in Alaska.

As soon as the gangplank was secured, a strange load of passengers began to descend. Dressed in ragged work clothes, their boots still caked with mud, their faces haggard and sun-blackened, they staggered down to the dock, pushing and hauling a queer assortment of baggage. Alone or in pairs they strained at weighty buckskin bags, old suitcases lashed with rope, and lumpy, blanket-wrapped bundles.

As they sweated past the silent, curious crowd on the dock, someone noted that all the newcomers wore the battered symbol of their trade, wide-brimmed miners' hats, and a whisper rippled among the onlookers. But when the first of the ragged crew hailed a four-horse wagon and called "Selby Smelting Works" to the driver, the whisper became a mighty roar.

"Gold!" "Gold from Alaska!"

Men ran behind the wagon, shouting the news. At the smelting works on Montgomery Street a mob crowded inside to gaze upon the streams of gold that spilled from bottles, tin cans, and leather bags onto the counters— to watch the clerks scoop up the glittering mass, weigh it, and pay for it on the spot.

Then the mob went wild. Through the streets they followed the prospectors. They besieged them in their hotels, swarming through halls and lobbies in the hope of catching a glimpse of the ragged men whom gold had made kings.

In two days, when a second steamer, the *Portland,* arrived in Seattle with two tons of gold on board, the news had been wired around the world and the great stampede to the Klondike gold fields of the Yukon was on. Men rushed to mortgage their homes, to borrow or beg a "stake." Doctors and lawyers deserted their practices to join the gold-crazed throngs. Policemen, preachers, clerks, barbers, city officials left their posts without a day's notice, scrambling for outfits and for a place on any ship going north. It was "Klondike or bust," and reason had no place in the mad cities during this week in July.

In the crowds that pushed through the waterfront and up and down the streets of San Francisco day and night was Jack London, aflame with the Klondike fever. Here was the miracle that he did not believe in. Gold! Adventure! Escape from the torment of his existence.

In a frenzy, he tried to sign onto a ship as seaman, but for every post there were a hundred applicants. Every rotten hull in the bay was being pressed into service, and still there was no place for him among the crews.

As he pushed into the hastily assembled supply stores and watched money pass over counters for the outfit that every Klondiker was told he must have, his agitation increased. Money! He had to beg for nickels to ride the ferry from Oakland. And yet a man must have at least a thousand pounds of gear—pick, short-handled shovels, tools, nails and other materials for making sleds and boats, woolen underwear, fur-lined coats, boots, and a year's supply of grub. The list was endless.

For days he flew from one friend to another. "You stake me and I'll bring out gold for both of us," was his plea. But who of his acquaintances had money for a stake? No one.

He bargained with the editors of newspapers but they laughed at him. Their best reporters were already packing to go north.

Fifty dollars for passage to Dyea at the head of the Lynn Canal, and the price was going up every hour! I could ride my bicycle over that Chilkoot Pass, he

thought desperately. Or pack right along with the Indians for the price of my grub. But how? How to get
there?

When at last he staggered into his house exhausted,
in a rage from frustration but still determined somehow
to go, he found that even his father lying in his bed had
caught the Klondike fever. "If I could just get onto one
of those ships," he whispered, "I'd get well. I know I
would!"

And his mother, ever ready to gamble her last cent
on anything that offered a chance for fortune, had the
glint of gold in her eyes. Only Eliza, the sober, practical
member of the family, would remain unmoved, Jack
believed.

But within an hour of Jack's return from San Francisco, as he sat wolfing the first good meal that he had
stopped to eat in two days, Captain Shepard, Eliza's
aging husband, thundered into the kitchen, followed
by Eliza. Breathing hard, he grasped Jack by the shoulders, his thin fingers digging into the flesh.

"Jack! Jack!" he cried. "If you'll go with me and
help me dig out that gold I'll stake us both."

Jack recoiled as he looked into the fanatical eyes of
his brother-in-law. Dig gold! Why, he couldn't pick up
a pin without panting. He had a bad heart, and he hadn't
used his muscles in many years.

Jack's eyes searched Eliza's face, but he saw only
resignation there. He needed time to think this out.

Why, he'd have to carry his own thousand-pound outfit and Captain Shepard's, too. Maybe he'd even have to
carry the Captain over Chilkoot Pass. And yet . . .
here was the chance that he had been searching for,
coming from a source that he'd never even thought of!

"Sit down, Captain, and let's talk about this," he said
with all the enthusiasm he could muster. "You know,
it'll cost a lot of money to get both of us up there. One—
maybe two thousand dollars, I figure, for a good outfit."

"We'll have the best!" the Captain cried. "We've got
some money saved, and Eliza says she'll mortgage the
house."

Jack looked at his sister in amazement. The house
belonged to her, he knew, paid for out of her hard-
earned money. He had been counting on her to back
him up.

"Tell you what I'll do, Captain," he offered. "If you'll
stake me, Eliza won't have to mortgage the house and
I'll work twice as hard for both of us. You can just sit
right here where it's nice and warm and listen for those
nuggets rolling into my shovel. And when I come back
you'll get half of every bit of gold I dig out."

The Captain's face flamed. "Sit here and miss all the
fun? Well, I guess not! I'm going to the Klondike or
die trying. I've got two berths on the *Umatilla* for the
twenty-fifth, and if you don't go with me, I'll get somebody else. Why, we can get in there and back with our
gold before winter!"

Jack shook his head. He knew better. But then he

gave up. He brought pencil and paper from his room, and until late that night they planned and argued. The Captain wanted one of the newfangled Klondike stoves made of sheet iron that folded into a neat pack. Jack insisted upon allowing space for books, as many as he could carry. And the two women wrangled over the amount of food that two men would need.

In the morning, while Jack scurried about for the books that he would take, Captain Shepard fainted on a streetcar on his way to the ferry terminal. A doctor was called. The elderly man had had a heart attack and was warned to stay in bed for two weeks. But in a few hours he was up again, shouting "Ho, for the Klondike" along with all the other mad stampeders in the supply stores along the waterfront, where nothing was too good for Captain Shepard and his partner. The thickest red flannels . . . the warmest fur-lined coats and caps . . . the finest evaporated milk, dried vegetables, flour. Jack sniffed skeptically at the sack of dried eggs that looked to him like cornmeal, but into the pack it went.

The next day they fought their way through the mobs on the San Francisco pier and scrambled aboard the *Umatilla,* riding low in the water with her tons of cargo filling every foot of space on deck and below.

Crammed against the rail, Jack and his partner waved good-by to Eliza on the dock below, her hat askew and almost smothered by the cheering, shouting crowds, but waving as wildly as any of the others.

Jack stole a glance at Eliza's frail, gray-faced husband

who was clutching the rail for support. And then he turned away and pulled a letter from his pocket. He had read it once and now he read it again. It was from Mabel Applegarth's mother, begging him not to go to Alaska, where he would surely die.

He laughed and thrust the letter back into his pocket. And then his eyes clouded. Where was a letter from Mabel? What did *she* want? But he did not need to ask.

She wants whatever her mother tells her to want, he thought. She'd like to have me give up my writing, settle down to a steady job as a bank clerk or something like that, wear stiff white collars and turn my back on the fellows who walk the streets looking for jobs. He sighed. After two whole years, she doesn't know me at all.

The *Umatilla* was swinging out into the bay and heading toward the Golden Gate. Jack took a deep breath of the tangy air. It had been nearly four years since he had come through the entrance to the bay on the *Sophia Sutherland,* wanting just what Mabel and her mother wanted for him now. A good job, a chance to work up, a nice home.

But I've traveled a long way since then, he told himself. A long, long way.

On the third of August, nine days after he had left San Francisco, Jack sat on the deck of the *City of Topeka* to which all the passengers and freight of the *Umatilla* had been transferred at Port Townsend, Washington.

His skin, made tender by weeks in the laundry and at his desk, was raw and already peeling. He patted his cheeks gingerly as his eyes swept over the forbidding shoreline of the Lynn Canal through which they were passing, and moved across the massive, glowering Chilkoot Mountains ahead. Then he quickly brought his attention back to the paper spread out on a heap of baggage in front of him.

Huddled over the paper were three other young men and the elderly Captain Shepard. During the first days on board, Jack had worked his way among the excited crowd, searching carefully for the partners that he knew he must have if he was to get his brother-in-law and a ton of gear to the interior of the Yukon. Those who argued and bragged, who had never worked with their hands, he passed by. But there were three . . . Merritt Sloper, small and wiry, knew shipbuilding; Fred Thompson and Jim Goodman were steady, hard-working fellows. The four had agreed to team up. Four . . . and, of course, Captain Shepard.

Now they sat, intent upon the paper that Jack traced with a pencil.

"Now, according to the guide book, here's where we land," he said. "Dyea Village. Indian. And here are the passes."

He drew a line almost directly north. "This is Chilkoot Pass. It's shorter, about twenty-eight miles from the beach to Lake Lindeman, but steeper. Goes right up thirty-five hundred feet, with snow and glaciers at the top."

He drew another line that curved to the right. "Here's White Pass. It's not so steep, but it's longer. About forty-five miles, I hear. Ends at Lake Bennett a little farther up. Now, fellows, we've got to make up our minds before we land. There'll be a stampede as soon as we hit the beach, and the first ones on the trail will get the best diggings. We've got to make time."

Captain Shepard's troubled eyes followed the longer line. From the hold of the ship, the neighing of frantic horses filled the air, and the others saw him wince.

"Those horses," he said. "They're for packing over White Pass, I've heard. Maybe I could ride."

Goodman snorted. "It'll be Dead Horse Pass if they try to use those skinny beasts. Bunch of old dray horses they rounded up, and after this trip they won't be worth much. Indians'll pack us over Chilkoot for five cents a pound, somebody told me. I vote we take the shorter pass and let the Indians do the work." He sniffed the air. "Smells like snow time already, and we've got a boat to build and three or four hundred miles of water to cover. I'd like to get my gold out of the ground before the freeze-up comes."

"Me, too," Sloper agreed. "My wife thinks I'm going to die up here any day, and I want to prove she's wrong."

"Chilkoot's for me," Fred Thompson chimed in.

"Grab the first Indians we see and get started, I say."

Jack looked at Shepard. "Let's see. That'll be about one hundred dollars for us, Captain. What do you say?"

The Captain nodded, but his eyes were searching the fog-shrouded peaks of the Chilkoot range and his thoughts seemed to be far away.

When the *City of Topeka* eased slowly toward the end of the canal in high tide, bedlam broke loose. Only a short time could she remain, for when the tide went out, forty or fifty feet of mud flats would separate the dry beach from the ship. When barges eased alongside, baggage was thrown over the side, helter-skelter. From the hold, screaming horses were lifted out and dropped into the water to swim for shore or sink. Men jumped into the barges after their baggage and were dumped on shore like so many logs.

In the wild excitement on the beach, Jack and his partners found each other and began to sort frantically through the tonnage before it slipped into the slime or was trampled under by the crowds that scrambled over it. Through the din, Jack could hear his brother-in-law's plaintive voice as he bargained with the stoic Indians who stood among the frantic stampeders. "How muchee?" "How muchee?" rang in his ears.

Piece by piece, the four younger partners dragged everything to dry ground, and by nightfall found that they were miraculously five miles above the beach with everything intact. Exhausted, they ripped open a package of food, wolfed whatever came to hand, rolled up in blankets, and fell asleep without making camp.

When Jack opened his eyes the next morning, the first thing he saw was his brother-in-law's thin frame bending over him.

"Jack," he wailed. "Those Indians! They're getting twenty-five—thirty cents a pound now! We can't . . ." He sank down to the ground and buried his face in his shaking hands.

Jack sat bolt upright.

"Six hundred dollars!" he cried. "Why, that'll clean us out before we get started. We'll have to pack over the trail ourselves."

The elderly man shook his head and then pointed a shaking finger out across the beach where groups of dejected men hovered over their stacks of mud-soaked gear. "Look at 'em. Half of 'em haven't got a chance. Tons of gear, and nobody to move it.

"I'm going home, Jack," he said in a hollow voice. "You take the grub and gear, and bring out that gold, boy, if there's any left . . ." His voice trailed off.

Jack looked quickly away to conceal the relief that must surely show on his face. With Captain Shepard, there was little chance of making it to Dawson before the freeze-up. Without him, and with three strong companions, he had a chance. He looked at the mob on the beach and thought of the thousands who would be following in a day . . . two days . . . All through

the fall they would be coming with pick and shovel to
search for gold. In his mind he could see a steady line
of desperate men moving up over that frozen pass and
down through ice-clogged rivers toward the Klondike.

But only the first of them, the hardiest, would get the
gold.

He sprang to his feet. "You're doing the right thing,
Captain. If you hurry, you can make it to the *Topeka*
before she leaves and have a nice trip back. Tell the
folks how things are and have 'em write me at Dawson.
We'll get up there and stake our claims before the rest
of this mob make it over the pass."

Quickly he untied ropes and straps and sorted out
the Captain's personal belongings. As his brother-in-
law staggered under his load toward the beach and the
barges that waited for the high tide to float them free,
he turned to the business of carefully rearranging his
entire outfit in packs that he could carry, one by one,
over that glistening, defiant ridge thirty-five hundred
feet above him.

All around him, grim and silent men were doing
likewise. For each one knew in his heart that, from here
on, success depended upon both brain and brawn. The
weak and the foolhardy among them would not survive.

Chapter 13

Across slippery moss and undergrowth . . . through knee-deep mud of icy streams to Pleasant Camp . . . over sharp loose shale to Sheep Camp . . . on to the last stopping place, The Scales, at the base of the glowering barrier of rock and glaciers. It was four miles up from The Scales to the notch in the sharp-edged rim that was Chilkoot Pass. Only at rare moments did Jack, bent under his one hundred and fifty pound loads, dare to raise his eyes from the trail to the slow-moving line of creatures crawling and clawing their way up the face of the mountain. Not once but time after time must each man drag to the top and then—slipping, sliding, rolling —descend, bruised and exhausted, to shoulder another load and start again.

Each mile was a grim and bitter drama of small success or heartbreaking defeat. Big, husky men sank down onto boulders and wept. Others, in a frenzy of despair, abandoned their possessions piece by piece. They strewed the paths but no one stopped to recover them as the line inched steadily upward.

At the top, shivering in the snow or rain that swirled continuously through the gap, Jack huddled in his fur-lined coat. But on the trail, sweating under his load, he sometimes stripped to his red flannels and startled the Indian packers as he passed them by at every opportunity. For under the deadening agony of the climb lay a spark of pride that prodded him to outpack the Indians. His stomach leaden with cold beans and flapjacks, he cached each load at the summit, marked it with a long pole, and went back again and again.

When the four men had cached their entire outfits at the summit, they began the descent. Across a glacier to Crater Lake . . . through rugged mountain trails that by-passed other lakes . . . up to their knees in shallow, marshy beaches . . . at last they reached the shore of Lake Lindeman.

At dusk on the final day, as Jack stirred the kettle of beans and bacon simmering on Captain Shepard's Klondike stove and watched tents rising like gray mushrooms from the damp shore of the lake, he thought of the Captain and shuddered. Could his brother-in-law, sitting now in the warmth of his own kitchen in Oakland and telling of the horrors of Dyea beach, imagine what surely would have been his fate had he tried to continue? Along that twenty-eight mile trail and down in the canyons lay the bodies of the unfit. Already word was coming in of worse horrors through White Pass, where the carcasses of cruelly driven horses lay thick among the boulders. Dead Horse Pass.

Merritt Sloper, who had been scouting, came back into camp and slumped down close to the fire. "The timber around here's too scrubby for a good boat," he announced. "Besides, there's some mean-looking rapids a mile or so up the way, full of boulders. We could wreck a loaded boat on 'em in a minute. Think we'd better go up Lake Bennett eight or nine miles before we start to build."

The others groaned. Here they were at the end of the grueling pack trail, they believed, and now Sloper proposed that they move on.

But he was adamant. "It's the middle of September, and we've got a lot of water to cover before the freeze-up. Maybe we can't make it anyway, but one setback and we stay right here until spring. Now I figure it this way —pack the tools and some grub to where we find good straight timber. Then two of us start the whipsaw going. We can take turns at it while we move the rest of the gear."

Jack saw the wisdom of his little hundred-pound partner's decision. "Sloper knows boat building," he said. "And I'm a sailor. I say, build strong. Anyway," he added, "when we put her in the water we'll be nine miles ahead of a lot of these fellows. And that's where we want to be—ahead of the whole mob all the way to Dawson!"

Goodman and Thompson reluctantly agreed.

Out of the green lumber that they whipsawed on the shore of Lake Bennett, the four men constructed a twenty-seven foot boat. When it was completed, many other boatbuilders along the shore dropped their tools to watch with envy as she slipped into the water and settled with perfect balance on the lapping waves. The proud owners christened her the *Yukon Belle* and then sweated into the dusk, working by the light of lanterns to lash their five thousand pounds of cargo on board and prepare to set out at dawn.

October was almost at hand. Thin ice crackled under their boots the next morning as the men quickly broke camp and shoved out into the chill water. As Jack hoisted the sail that he had fashioned from a large piece of canvas and watched the breeze fill it, a great smile broke over his face.

"Ho, for the Klondike!" he bellowed, and his words echoed back and forth across the water.

Indians stood in wonder and contempt as boat after boat sailed out across their once-silent lake, headed north into the wintry land that wise birds had already deserted. For they knew that each morning the ice along the shore would grow wider and thicker, and the white blizzards would soon descend to halt all passage until spring. But the white men, filled with a lust that knew no reason, would not listen to their warnings.

The four men were almost gleeful as Jack sailed their boat across Lake Bennett and Lake Marsh. After nearly two months of incessant toil, for long stretches they would be able to rest their aching muscles and nurse their blistered hands in fur-lined mittens.

Jack held to the steering oar, determined to pass every boat on the lakes. Sixty Mile River lay ahead with its dreaded Miles Canyon and White Horse Rapids that they had heard about, but the *Yukon Belle* was strongly built and none of the four doubted her ability to carry them through.

Lake Marsh narrowed at its northern end into the river, and as Jack watched the other boats converge on the entrance, he called upon all of his sailor skill to reach the point first, ordering out the oars whenever the breeze slackened. The river, he had heard, was deep and swift, and the current would carry them along as soon as they reached it. But some of the landlubbers who were attempting to navigate their crude boats could hold back the *Yukon Belle* for days.

As he skimmed past a heavily loaded barge wallowing deep in the water, he waved a triumphant mittened hand and then concentrated on the tugging current of the river.

Suddenly they rounded a sharp bend where the water narrowed to about one hundred yards. Ahead was the canyon they had heard about—sheer towering walls only eighty feet apart through which the river roared.

Jim Goodman and Fred Thompson, at the oars, quickly maneuvered into an eddy where dozens of boats were already tied up. The canyon was empty, but several hundred men were portaging their outfits on their backs over narrow paths atop the canyon walls in preference to risking destruction in the raging water.

"Portage!" Goodman cried. "Why, it'll take us two —maybe three days to drag everything over the trail. And carry the *Yukon Belle?* How'll we do that?"

Merritt Sloper pulled off his cap and scratched his head. "How long do you figure it'd take us to run her through, Jack?" he asked.

Jack walked ahead for a distance and gazed down at the water pouring like dark oil between the sheer walls. The pressure of so much water being forced through this narrow passage caused it to rise six to eight feet into a ridge or hogback down the center.

"If we can hold her to the ridge . . . couple of minutes, maybe," he answered.

All around them, men were giving advice and warnings. "Last two boats that tried to make it cracked up. Everybody drowned!" "There's a whirlpool halfway through. Get into that and you're done for."

Jack walked back to the *Yukon Belle* with his three companions. "What do you say, men?" he asked.

Goodman was still sputtering. "I'd rather crack up and have done with it than portage," he said.

"Me, too," Thompson agreed. "If I was scared of a

little thing like a canyon, I'd have stayed right at home."

Sloper laughed. "My wife's sure I'm done for, so let's go!"

"All right," Jack agreed. "But if I'm going to pilot her, you'll have to do what I say."

First he insisted that they take down the sail and lash the canvas over everything. Then he stationed Sloper in the bow with a paddle and the other two at the oars. For the start, he called in the oars, and, lashing his own steering oar so that he could not lose it, shoved off while spectators lined up along the cliff.

At once they were caught by the swift current and sucked into the roaring, rampaging water. The loaded boat plunged and bucked through the sharp waves that creased the ridge. Little Merritt Sloper, perched in the bow, paddled wildly, sometimes thrusting his blade into a wave that almost submerged him, sometimes taking a swing into the air when the bow rose over a foaming crest.

As they hit the edge of the whirlpool, the *Yukon Belle* veered toward the cliff, and Jack heard his oar crack as he swung all his weight on it. Sloper, bobbing in the bow, snapped his paddle as they flew down the gutter barely two yards from the wall.

On through the canyon they plunged, slithering from side to side on the ridge. And then, in a moment, they found themselves settling quietly against a bank. Two minutes, and they had saved two days of hard labor!

Jubilant, they bailed out and headed for White Horse

Rapids. Here, as before, they found everyone portaging, skidding boats along the trail on tree trunks. But Jack's three companions, confident now that their captain could take them through this even more dangerous passage, would not hear of stopping.

Again onlookers lined the banks while, equipped with new paddles, they rushed from one whirlpool to another, missing destruction by inches. Toward the last, they flew a full circle in the sweep of a whirlpool and then shot into the end of the rapids, the Mane of the Horse, and again landed in a quiet eddy below.

This time they were chastened; they had had enough. But luckily there were no more rapids to run. Ahead lay Lake Laberge that flowed quietly into the Yukon River. Behind was the great bulk of the gold-seekers still packing the trails.

When they had bailed out again and set their sail for the final lake crossing before they could depend upon a current to carry them to Dawson, Jack raised his eyes to a white mist that was blowing in from the north, and frowned.

"Pull out the oars," he commanded. "Looks like a blizzard heading down the lake."

He had scarcely spoken when the storm struck, sending up mountainous waves that tinkled in slivers of ice as they descended on board. For three days the *Yukon Belle* was driven back. But on the fourth, when a crust of ice began to form on the surface of the water, they rowed through the night. And in the dawn, as they entered the Yukon River, they looked back exhausted but triumphant to see their path already glazed behind them.

"Poor devils," Jack said, thinking of the thousands of gold-seekers laboring over the trails between the Yukon River and Dyea. "Frozen in for the winter."

Luckily the blizzard moved south and the Yukon, flowing north, carried the heavily loaded boat along her shallow, sluggish bed. Light snow sprinkled the river bank and piled up in the mountains. Overhead the last of the wild geese winged south in ragged V-shaped formations, and now and then a herd of caribou plunged into the river and swam across, headed southward. Cakes of ice floated down from the tributaries of the great river and followed alongside, while each morning the crust at the river's edge grew steadily wider.

Occasionally an old boat loomed out of the gray mist of the river, its ragged occupants rowing frantically against the sluggish current. "There's no grub in Dawson!" was the cry that reached the four astonished companions. They shouted back warnings of ice in the lakes and thousands of stampeders frozen in along the pass, but the hungry Klondikers pressed on. Like the birds and the caribou, they followed the age-old instinctive call of food, and continued south.

Spirits on the *Yukon Belle* grew daily more gloomy as the men sailed toward the city from which others were fleeing.

"How'll we pan gold out of that ice?" Jim Goodman moaned each morning as he surveyed the growing white rim at the river's edge. "Six months—maybe seven before we'll see water again when this river freezes over."

Thompson worried over the problems of food and shelter. "Our tents'll never do. Snow'll bust 'em wide open. We'll have to build a good tight cabin, stake our claims, and then wait for spring. Our grub'll hold out if we're careful. But I don't know. When a mob of men get hungry they don't care whose grub they take."

Jack, alone, remained cheerful. He had been hungry before, and the gold could wait. The great white silence of the land in which men pitted themselves against the brute force of nature fascinated him. For centuries this struggle had been going on, but for the first time he was witnessing it.

In the cities that he knew, men struggled with each other for mastery. Corruption and greed—those were the overlords. But here no man could stop the ice from forming or the sun from growing dimmer each day.

"Just think of it," he said, his smile cracking his frost-chapped face. "Nothing to do all winter but cook our beans and bacon, chop a little wood, and rest. I could sleep for a month!"

The dreams of warm bunks and supper cooking on a hot stove came true sooner than the four sailors had anticipated. Off the east bank of the Yukon near the entrance to the Stewart River they came upon two islands. On Upper Island they sighted a group of cabins of a type that had been deserted by Bering Sea fur traders at points along the route. From the chimneys, welcoming smoke rose among the trees, and as they put in to the landing, men gathered at the shore to greet them.

"How far to Dawson?" Sloper called.

"About eighty miles. You're not thinking of going there, are you?" one of the men answered.

"Why not?" Goodman asked. "That's where the gold is, we hear. We're headed for Bonanza Creek to stake claims."

The crowd laughed good-naturedly.

"Bonanza. Every inch of the creek's been staked since the day after Carmack's strike. And all the other creeks around there, too. Folks are *leaving* Dawson. Haven't you heard?"

The four men looked at each other. They had heard, but they hadn't wanted to believe.

One man stepped forward from the group on shore. "I'm Doctor Harvey," he said.

Jack leaped out of the boat and shook the doctor's hand. Then the introductions began. As Jack clasped the hands of Judge Sullivan, Bert Hargrave, Emil Jensen, Elam Harnish, and a dozen others, their genuine friendliness warmed him. He had not realized how starved he was for good talk about something more than weather, food, and shelter.

A consultation was going on among a few of the men. Finally one said, "Dawson's no place to spend the winter, men. They're short on food and it's going to get worse. If you want to settle and then go up to see for yourselves, there's one cabin still empty that you're welcome to."

"You mean we've come all this way and the gold's all gone?" Sloper cried.

"There's more than one creek in the Yukon with gold in it," someone answered. "We're going up the Henderson to stake. You can come along if you want to."

That settled it. In short order, for there were many hands to help, the food, tools, and clothing were transferred from the *Yukon Belle* to a snug eighteen-foot cabin in a clearing.

Jack chose a bunk near the light of the fire and arranged his books on a little shelf above it: Darwin's *Origin of the Species,* Spencer's *First Principles,* Shakespeare . . . No light reading here, but books to challenge the mind during the long winter nights. Books to think about and read again.

Someone brought in a pail of fermenting sour dough and hung it behind the stove. Better than soda or yeast, here was the stuff for making bread and flapjacks, to be renewed with a little dough from each batch of bread and shared with the next newcomer. Soon a sharp odor filled the room, the smell of every "sourdough's" cabin in the Yukon.

JACK LONDON

In a few days they went up Henderson Creek, staked what appeared to be likely plots, and then sailed the greatly lightened *Yukon Belle* to Dawson to record their claims and satisfy themselves about conditions there.

Up and down the snow-packed streets of the metropolis of the North Jack wandered while famished, savage dogs snapped at his heels. He looked in at Bill McPhee's Pioneer Saloon where hungry, sick men took turns sleeping on benches and table, their sacks of gold stacked in the corners of the dark, airless room. Down the street, in the Yukon Hotel, where Lucky Swede's hoard of two hundred thousand dollars' worth of dust from Eldorado Creek was piled, men slept in double-decked filthy bunks under the rafters. At the bars, there was whiskey but no food. He saw sacks of gold dust thrown upon the counter and watched men lose fortunes at cards with a shrug of the shoulders.

In the dance halls, where light and music could be found, he moved among the homesick men and heard their stories. A partner had raced to file his claim in weather fifty degrees below zero and had frozen his lungs. Another was dying of scurvy in Father Judge's little hospital. A hundred tales of success and of failure he listened to, until the whole picture of the early days before news of the big strike reached the outside world became incredibly real. Here men had pitted themselves against unyielding nature. For every hardy or lucky soul who had won there were a dozen or more who had lost.

200

His mind full of the stories he had heard, Jack returned to Upper Island with the others to wait for spring. If the Henderson Creek claim did not pan out, he would seek another. He was strong and well, and he had learned enough, now, to make him wary. Back in the cabin there were books to read, and in the other cabins there was companionship.

The six months of winter were long and dark. In the few hours of feeble light the men on Upper Island chopped wood and repaired their cabins. But when the temperature dropped to fifty and sixty degrees below zero they ventured outside for only brief moments, wrapping their faces in wool scarves to prevent their lungs from freezing. Even so, there were frozen toes and fingers among them.

Inside the cabins men sharpened their tools to razor edge, overhauled their gear, built furniture, and wrangled with each other. As the days wore on and the last supplies of dried fruit and vegetables disappeared, signs of illness began to show and tempers grew shorter.

Jack read his own books and all the other books in camp and long into the night led discussions on many subjects. His feet wore paths between the cabins and his bright smile enlivened many a morose gathering. Here were hardy men with many adventures to recount, and he listened to their stories and learned from them.

The largest of the cabins belonged to Louis Savard,

a French Canadian, who spoke with an accent that delighted Jack. When Savard's dog, Nig, played one of his many tricks upon his master and goaded him to strange and colorful language, Jack would throw back his head and laugh, repeating the words carefully to fix them in his memory.

"That Nig is smarter than you are, Louis," he said one night when Savard came storming into his cabin after the canny dog had deserted him and his loaded sled thirty miles up a trail.

"You smart aleck, too," Savard snapped.

Now and then half-frozen stampeders staggered into camp, to be revived with food and warmth. Jack, stirring up sour dough flapjacks or pushing more wood into the red-hot stove, listened and asked questions. What happened in a man's mind when he lost his last match and the temperature was fifty below? What must a man do when he stumbles into a snow-covered water hole? How many minutes will he live if he cannot build a fire and dry his boots?

It was always the great battle for survival that intrigued him. The answers he recorded in his memory.

In the spring, before the ice broke on the river, Bert Hargrave began to show signs of the dreaded scurvy— the flabby skin and aching muscles were unmistakable. There were no fresh vegetables or fruit in the frozen north, but fresh meat would help.

Jack and Doctor Harvey set out with borrowed sled

and dogs to search for game. They traveled eighty miles before they brought down an elk. And then, the sled loaded with fresh meat, they turned back toward camp.

On the last night, as they sat beside a campfire before rolling up in fur robes to sleep away their weariness, Doctor Harvey asked, "What are you going to do with your gold, Jack, if you find it?"

Jack was silent for a moment. He had never put into words what had motivated him to undertake this mad adventure.

"I don't know," he finally answered. "I haven't really thought it out. First, of course, I'll pay my sister and brother-in-law their share. And I'll get the best doctors for Pa. Maybe get a house for my folks to live in so they won't have to worry about the rent any more."

"But what about yourself, Jack? What will you buy for yourself?"

Jack thought for a while. "Books, I guess. A suit of clothes. And time . . ."

"What do you mean—time?"

Jack laughed. "It's this way, Doc. For years I've worked so that I could have a little piece of time—time to study, to write, to think, to go sailing. Yeh, that's what I want—time."

The next day as they neared camp with their fresh meat, Jack was unusually silent. Time . . . but how much did he have? For several days he had felt the unmistakable twinges in his legs. His gums were sore and·

bleeding, and the flesh on his arms felt soft and putty-like. Now, at the end of the long trek, his breath was unnaturally short. When the elk meat was shared with the men in camp, what then? How long does a man with scurvy survive?

Soon Bert Hargrave was taken to Dawson by dog sled, and Jack moved in with Doctor Harvey. In May, as soon as the ice began to break, the two men, both now crippled by scurvy, painfully pulled down their cabin, made a raft from the logs, and said good-by to their camp mates.

"We'll be back," they called as they floated out through dangerous ice jams toward Dawson where they hoped to find relief.

"Strange thing about scurvy," the doctor explained. "It clears up miraculously with a little fresh food. Some-day we'll understand what happens, but now all we know is the quick cure. Maybe a shipload of food has got up the river by now. But it'll be worth its weight in gold."

Jack, trying to maneuver the clumsy raft through the rising ice-choked waters of the Yukon, looked down at his twisted right leg. He could not straighten it but must hobble along, putting all his weight on his toes.

"Gold! A potato or a lemon would mean more to me right now than a Bonanza claim."

In Dawson the two crippled companions sold their raft to a sawmill for a few hundred dollars, the price of a small sack of potatoes if they could find them. At Father Judge's little hospital they shared a potato and a lemon.

"You must leave at once," the kindly priest told Jack. "Two little steamers have come through, but they were loaded with whiskey and mining tools and the mail. Men are dying every day, and there's no telling when we'll get relief."

Give up? Return home empty-handed?

"A whole year of my life wasted," he moaned to Doctor Harvey.

"Nothing's wasted," the older man answered. "Just add this one to all those other experiences you've told me about. Come on, let's see if there's any mail for us."

A line of men waiting for word from home stretched the length of the waterfront while harried Mounted Police attempted to sort out thousands of letters that had been brought in by the first little steamer. Jack and his companion decided to take turns waiting in line. Meanwhile, using an old rowboat they had found, they would pull logs from the river to sell to the sawmill.

On the third day, when Jack emerged from the little post office with a handful of letters, he hobbled down to the boat, gave the doctor his mail, and read his own letters one by one.

When he finished, he sat staring into the mush-ice of the flooding river.

"Bad news?" Harvey asked.

"Pa's dead. Six months ago, and I didn't know all this time. I was going to get the best doctors for him."

The doctor touched his arm sympathetically. "Nobody could have saved him," he said. "An old man with bad lungs. There's nothing we can do."

Jack picked up his letters and sorted through them again. There was other news. Captain Shepard had reached home safely and was in better health. Everyone was excited about the sinking of a battleship called the *Maine* off the coast of Cuba in February. So long ago! They expected war to be declared, and Fred Jacobs was planning to enlist.

I ought to get home. Ma needs me, he told himself. If I die from scurvy up here, what'll she do?

But he stayed on a little longer.

At last he knew he was defeated. It was June when he waved good-by to Doctor Harvey and, in company with two other men, set out in a leaky rowboat to drift with the six-mile current down the nineteen hundred miles of the Yukon River. In about three weeks they should reach St. Michael, he believed. With luck and a little fresh food he could work his way down the coast on a steamer, to arrive home, sick and penniless, a wasted year behind him.

But as the current carried the little boat along and Jack lay under the netting listening to the mosquitoes swarm above him, he began to think of all that he had seen and done, of all the stories he had heard. And the old desire to write began to return.

Painfully, day by day, he recorded in a little notebook details of the trip from Dawson to the sea, marking in the margin the names of magazines that might be interested. *Outing* . . . *Youth's Companion* . . . The customs of the Indians, the types of birds, the appearance of a Russian Mission—hundreds of details went into the little book to keep alive a spark of hope as he floated down the river.

Chapter **14**

One afternoon, two months later, Jack London pushed through the door of the Oakland library and stood bareheaded in the September sunlight. A thick bank of fog was slowly moving in from the ocean, and his glazed eyes watched it inch its way across the yellow sun until the last ray was obliterated. He shivered and turned up his coat collar. A chill ran down his spine and he leaned against the building for a moment while he tried to take in what he had just heard from Mr. Bamford.

Fred Jacobs—gone. It could not be true, and yet it was. The newspaper account stated it plainly. One man, only one, had died of fever en route to Manila on that troop ship. Fred Jacobs.

Pictures of his slightly built, studious friend swam through Jack's thoughts: Fred moving quietly about the library . . . sitting bent over a book . . . lying in the grass while he talked of his plans to be a chemist after he graduated from the university.

Slowly Jack moved down the steps toward the bicycle rack while his mind tried to make some sense out of this thing that had happened. Why—why—should Fred, on his first adventure, be stricken, while he, Jack London, be permitted to survive typhoons, the wheels of fast-moving trains, the churning waters of White Horse Rapids, and crippling scurvy? Why should he stand now in almost perfect health while Fred lay dead?

He shook his head from side to side in bewilderment. If there was an answer, he could not find it yet.

As he mounted his wheel, he knew, vaguely, that he should go to Bess to comfort her. But what could he say to her? If Ted Applegarth were here they could go together. Or Mabel—she would know just what to say.

Jack turned his wheel toward East Oakland while his mind explored the strange, unpredictable world in which he lived. Each time he returned from an adventure, he seemed to face a new life. There was the inevitable new home to adjust to, this one smaller than ever at 962 East Sixteenth Street. As though symbolic of the life he had returned to, his room had shrunk, too. This one in which he slept and worked was only ten feet square. And friends? Fred gone. Ted and Mabel moved to College Park, forty miles away. Only Bess, now sorrowing, remained of the old happy group.

The only thing that was constant, that he could always depend upon returning to, was the little Oakland library.

And poverty. That I can always depend upon, too, he

thought bitterly. Poverty, and the fear of having to go back to coal shoveling.

Quietly Jack let himself into the house. His mother was off somewhere, and with relief he shut himself into his tiny room and threw himself onto the bed while the old battle within him between duty and fulfillment continued. The desire to write was stronger than ever but as the desire grew, the forces that seemed always lined up against him grew stronger, too.

Since he had returned in July there had been no question in his or anyone's mind. He must find work to support himself and his mother. But how? Where? The unemployed roamed the streets in greater numbers now. Hunger haunted the faces of men, women, and children at employment offices. He had tried everything, but he had no trade. Laundries, even the mills turned him away. There were no jobs on the waterfront. He ran advertisements in the newspapers: "WANTED—Any kind of work; will type-write reasonably. Receive and deliver same." But nothing came of that either.

Jack wandered out to the kitchen, picked up a raw potato, and washed it at the sink. Wearily he opened the newspaper and turned to the Help Wanted section again. Once in a while he found an odd job there that no one else wanted—a day's work for a few coins. But usually, for any job listed, a long line of desperate men waited through the night for a door to open and admit one or two.

With a pencil he circled a few items in the brief Help Wanted column and then his eyes wandered on down the page. At the bottom they stopped.

"Civil Service examination for mail carrier," he read aloud. "Monday, nine A.M., Post Office Building."

Carefully Jack tore the small notice from the bottom of the sheet, read it again, and tucked it into his shirt pocket. Mail carrier. Into his mind came pictures of himself, dressed in a gray uniform, leather bags strapped to his shoulders as he trod the streets of Oakland delivering the mail from door to door. No reading. No writing until evening when, feet swollen and blistered, he might prop himself onto the bed and try to marshal his thoughts before his eyes began to droop.

And yet—and yet—there would be meat on the table each night when he got home. And the grim line of his mother's thin lips would soften. He could retrieve his watch from the pawnbroker, and his father's mackintosh, too, before the winter rains started once more. He could buy stamps and paper, perhaps in time even a decent suit to wear on Sundays for occasional trips to College Park.

And Mabel? Bitterly Jack admitted to himself that Mabel would be pleased. In spite of her fluttering encouragement, he knew full well that she had never believed he could succeed as a writer.

He bit off a chunk of raw potato and chewed it pensively while he continued to think about Mabel Applegarth. There was no doubt that during the past year his feeling toward her had changed. It had begun to change even before he left for the Klondike, he now realized. He still wrote to her and sent copies of some of his stories and poems. Her carefully worded letters full of advice about his future and childish criticism of his writing came regularly by return mail.

But as the weeks passed, his old worshipful attitude was slowly ebbing away. Once he had valued her criticism of his writing and had tried to follow her advice. But gradually, as his own knowledge broadened and deepened, he had come to realize how narrow and shallow her outlook was and how little she really knew.

Jack popped the last of the potato into his mouth and champed it angrily. The trouble, he told himself, is that we have no common ground. She doesn't understand me, and she never will.

The thought made him sadder than before, and lonelier. Now that Fred Jacobs was gone, there was no one left who really understood him.

He pulled the notice from his pocket and read it again. "Monday, nine A.M., Post Office Building."

All right, he decided. I'll take that examination and make everybody happy. But while I'm waiting to find out if I pass, I'll fight my battle alone. Maybe just one of those silent, sullen people who run the magazines will save me from becoming a mail carrier.

Compared with the examinations that he had taken

at the university, the civil service examination on Monday morning seemed very easy to Jack, and he came away from it confident that he had done well. On the way home he questioned the postman on his street and learned that a beginner received forty-five dollars a month, but the regular salary, after six months, would be sixty-five dollars.

Sixty-five dollars! That's a lot of money for a ten-cents-an-hour man, he told himself. The kind of job I used to dream about.

But now he had other dreams, and carrying the mail did not fit into them.

Jack wrote to Mabel at once, and as he had predicted, her prompt reply was enthusiastic. It was his duty, she said, to settle down to steady employment if he wished to be well thought of by worthwhile people. Angrily he tossed the letter aside.

His mother's reaction was the one that surprised him. The thought of having sixty-five dollars a month besides her small widow's pension so overjoyed her that any ordinary job seemed insignificant.

"Now you just stop running around looking for anything else," she said. "I've got the pension, and the landlady and the grocers can wait for their money. Eliza will—"

"No!" Jack exploded. "Eliza's done enough for us. I owe her too much now. We'll go on short rations."

Here was the chance that he needed—that piece of

time that he had told Doctor Harvey he wanted above all else. Up there in the great white silence of the Yukon, when they sat beside their campfire, his explanation had seemed adequate. With time he could write the stories that were everywhere around him.

But now that he was at home again, remembering all of the rejected manuscripts that lay in his bureau drawers, he knew that he needed more than time to write. He needed time to learn *how* to write stories that would sell. But how could he learn? There was no one to teach him.

I'll just have to start over again and find out for myself, he resolved. Find out how the other fellows do it. Writing's a business. I've got to learn it from the ground up with no overseers telling me what to do.

With new determination to master this problem as he had mastered others, Jack went to the library and brought home armloads of magazines. He read them critically, and when he came upon a story that satisfied him he studied it in detail, outlining the plot, copying parts of the dialogue, counting the words. Soon he realized that most of the stories in magazines followed much the same pattern, and he made out lists of plots for himself.

Rudyard Kipling was one of the most popular writers of the time, and he was also one of Jack's favorite authors. For days he copied page after page of Kipling's stories until he began to get the swing of his style and feel the flow of words beneath his pencil.

But Kipling used words that he had never thought of, and as he saw them come onto the page he knew what he must do. As he read and copied and analyzed, he wrote each new word that he found on a slip of paper and looked up the pronunciation and meaning in his dictionary. He stuck the slips of paper into the frame of his mirror, tacked them to the wall over his table, and hung lists of them on a wire strung across his bed where he could see them when he first opened his eyes in the morning. Everywhere his eyes turned there were words . . . words . . . He repeated them over and over, used them in sentences, and when he had mastered them, replaced them with new ones.

When the grocer refused his mother more credit and the landlady's little girl knocked each day at the door for the rent, Jack broke off his study to write furiously again. He sent an article called "Down the River" to a San Francisco newspaper; it was the story of his trip from Dawson to St. Michael. In one week he wrote a twenty-one-thousand-word serial for *Youth's Companion* and pawned his bicycle for rent of a typewriter and stamps. From his stack of old manuscripts he pulled out a horror story, "By a Thousand Deaths," retyped it, and sent it to the *Black Cat*.

And then in November he wrote a Klondike story and named it "To the Man on Trail." It was not like any of the stories that he had been studying. The characters he derived from the men he had known on Upper Island. Louis Savard, with his colorful broken English, became

Louis Savoy. Some of the qualities of Emil Jensen and of himself, too, he gave to Malemute Kid. The rough speech and raucous laughter of the camp, the snarling, famished dogs, the grim contest between men in temperature seventy-four degrees below zero all came to the pages as he remembered them.

But who would take such a story? Eastern publishers might keep it for weeks and then return it without comment. There was the *Overland Monthly,* published just across the bay in San Francisco. It was a fine magazine, founded by the writer Bret Harte. He had never aimed so high; but now, his nerves on edge from poor food and anxiety, with nothing left to pawn and rent overdue on the typewriter, he used the last of his stamps to send his story across the bay.

By the end of November, Jack was half sick and so nervous that his hands shook when he tried to write. The mail, for which he waited in agony each day, brought nothing—no word from Washington on how he stood in the examinations, no word from the *Youth's Companion,* from the *Black Cat,* from the San Francisco newspaper about his article.

When he heard the cheerful mailman pass the house each morning, whistling, his mood grew blacker.

"He can whistle," he snarled. "He'll have steak for his dinner."

But one morning early in December, a letter arrived. As Jack pulled the thin envelope from the box and read

Overland Monthly on the upper left-hand corner, his knees began to shake. Slowly he turned around, walked stiffly back into his room, and sank down onto the bed.

He turned the letter over and over in his hands. They hadn't returned his manuscript. They had kept it!

Now don't get your hopes up, he warned himself. Maybe they don't pay two cents a word. Maybe only one cent. For my four thousand words, that'll be . . .

He ripped open the letter and shook it out. There was no check. He skimmed the words quickly: ". . . greatly pleased by your story . . . will publish in January issue . . . five dollars . . ."

"Five dollars for four thousand words," Jack shouted. "The best story I ever wrote! Only *five* dollars."

He ripped the envelope apart and shook it savagely. There was no check. Not two cents for a stamp with which to send a reply. Not five cents for fare to San Francisco.

Jack raged through the house and out into the street. When he could walk no more he stumbled home, threw himself across his bed, and slept.

After a bleak December, marked by daily resolutions to go back to coal-shoveling, January brought news from Washington. Jack had passed first in the examination for mail carrier. As soon as there was a vacancy, he would be called.

The *Youth's Companion* returned his serial, but enclosed a letter of explanation instead of the usual rejection slip. A few days later, another thin envelope arrived, this one from the *Black Cat*. They would pay forty dollars for his four-thousand-word story if he would permit them to cut it in half.

Elated, Jack rushed to the barber shop down the street to borrow a little money for stamps. They could cut it as much as they wanted to, if only they would send the money at once, he replied.

When the check arrived by return mail, Jack forgot about coal-shoveling, collected his coat, watch, and bicycle from the pawnshop, and buckled down to work again. "To the Man on Trail" in the January issue of the *Overland Monthly* inspired him to send another Malemute Kid story across the bay accompanied by an appeal for payment.

"The White Silence" appeared in the February issue, but still no check arrived. Infuriated, Jack jammed his cap onto his head and set out for the San Francisco ferry. All the way across the bay, he fumed. A first-rate magazine. They'd better pay up, he told himself. They can't steal my stuff and get away with it.

But by the time he reached the little office, he had cooled off somewhat. Publication in a first-rate magazine was important. His friends were already congratulating him. On Sunday night, when he had broken off work to go down to the Labor party meeting, he had noticed a new respect in the attitude of some of the men.

I don't want to lose out, he decided. But I've got to have the money.

Inside the small *Overland Monthly* office, a white-haired man sat on a high stool, intent upon a ledger. Unnoticed, Jack hesitated for a moment before he blurted out, "I'm Jack London and I've come to get the money for my two stories."

The man swung around and stared at the intruder. And then slowly he rose, a look of disbelief on his face as his eyes ran over the shabby clothes, the haggard cheeks and hollow eyes.

"You're . . . you're Jack London? Why I thought . . . we thought . . ."

"I've come for my money," Jack repeated.

"Well now, Mr. London . . . you see . . . we pay on publication."

Jack's blood began to rise, and he clenched his fist.

"They're published aren't they? I read 'em in your magazine. And now I want my money!"

The man cleared his throat. "We'll send you a check very soon, Mr. London," he said quietly.

Jack's hand began to tremble and he thrust it into his empty pocket. He was hungry and without even a nickel for the ferry back to Oakland.

He set his jaw. "No! I want it now. I've got to have it." His face flamed with anger.

The man's eyes wavered and he reached into his own pocket. "Our editor, Mr. Bridge, has just returned from the East," he said meekly. "He has expressed a wish to meet you."

At that moment the editor himself came from an inner room. Evidently he had overheard the conversation, for he, too, had his hand in his pocket. The two men, editor and business manager, counted their money. One . . . two . . . three . . . The dollars moved across the counter toward Jack, and when he had ten in his own pocket, felt them jingle in his fingers, he threw back his head and smiled. Ten dollars for meat and stamps. Ten dollars for a little more time.

"Thank you," he said as he turned to leave.

But Mr. Bridge opened the gate and motioned toward the inner office. "Come in, Mr. London," he said. "I've been wanting to have a talk with you."

An hour later, Jack walked out of the *Overland Monthly* office with a much clearer picture of the profession that he was trying to hammer his way into. And during that hour he had come to an agreement with the editor that made sense to him.

A first-rate magazine was not always a wealthy one, he learned. The *Overland Monthly* was managing to keep alive, month by month, only because its writers were willing to exchange their stories for the prestige that publication in its pages gave them. But if Jack would supply six more stories that could be published in the next six issues, for the low rate of seven dollars and fifty cents each, the editor would see that he had a prominent place in the magazine and publicity from reviewers and critics. All this, he was told, would bring his work to the attention of other editors who could afford to pay more.

While Jack ate the first steak that he had tasted in a long time and later stood out in the crisp air on the forward deck of the Oakland ferry, the harassed look gradually left his face. Recalling the many fine things the editor had said about his stories, he began to realize that he was on his way up at last. It was only a matter of time. If he and his mother could hold out a little longer, if the call did not come from the post office for a few more months, he might win through.

Chapter 15

Before Jack London's bright new optimism could fade, another letter arrived, this one postmarked Harold, California. It was a brief note from someone who signed his name "Cloudesley Johns." He had read Jack's two stories in the *Overland Monthly* and he prophesied greatness for the author.

Enormously cheered, Jack tacked the letter over his desk where he could see it every time he looked up from his work. He answered it immediately. *Someone* besides the men at the *Overland* liked his stories, liked them enough to sit down and write him a letter! Remembering Mabel's criticism of "To the Man on Trail" he felt doubly happy.

Thus began a friendship, by mail, that did more for Jack than any check from a publisher could possibly have done. He was no longer alone; someone understood. With Cloudesley Johns, a young man who was also learning to write, he freely discussed many things that he had never been able to talk about with Mabel or Ted or anyone else: their methods of composing, their opinions of other writers, their likes and dislikes, their hopes and failures.

Gradually, as Jack's correspondence with Cloudesley increased, his letters to Mabel dwindled. He found that he no longer looked forward to hearing from her, and he put off the task of replying. Another phase of his life was drawing to a close.

Meanwhile, to his relief, his mother's attitude was undergoing a change. Her son was a writer whose stories were being printed in a fine magazine. She who had urged him to write his first story now had proof of her good judgment to show to her doubting neighbors.

But just when life was beginning to look brighter, the call to go to work came from the post office.

Jack paced back and forth through the house. "What'll I do, Ma?" he cried. "I'm getting ahead—you can see that. A check every month from the *Overland* and some more stuff in the mail that I haven't heard from. I can't give up now, can I?"

Flora London sighed. Sixty-five dollars a month was a lot of money. But her gambler's instinct found a possible solution.

"Maybe you can get them to pass you over this time," she suggested. "There ought to be another vacancy before long."

Jack stared at her, amazed. And then he raced out of the house and down to the post office before his courage failed him.

There he explained his plight to an indifferent postmaster.

"You don't want the job?" the man asked coldly.

"Yes, I *do* want it, don't you see? If you could just call me the next time there's . . ."

The postmaster sat down at his desk and picked up his pen.

"If you want it, you'll take it," he said flatly.

Jack set his jaw. Couldn't this fellow understand? Was he just a piece of machinery without a heart?

After an interminable silence, the postmaster looked up again. "Well?" he asked.

"I won't take it," Jack blurted out, his face flaming.

Outside the building, when he had cooled off, he realized with horror what he had done. Like the gamblers he had seen in Dawson—like his own mother—he had staked the riches of sixty-five dollars of grub money on a shaky chance.

And yet he realized that, in spite of what lay ahead, he felt good about what he had done, better than he had felt through all the months of waiting.

That fellow was right, he told himself. He saw through me. If I'd wanted that job I'd have taken it and buckled on the mail sacks. But I didn't want it. I'd have hated every day of being a mail carrier.

"I'm in business for myself, now," he told Eliza as he stopped by her house to explain and to see if she had an old bookkeeper's ledger that she could give him. "Have to set up books."

She laughed. "I never saw anybody so happy over turning down a sixty-five-dollar-a-month job. You must think this new business is going to pay off. How many accounts do you have?"

"Paid or pending?" he joked. "Let's see. Six paid—four stories and two poems to *Town Topics*. About thirty pending. I'm working on some articles about learning to write. I figure I ought to know as much about that subject as anybody."

He rummaged through a cupboard on the back porch and found a roll of stiff wire. "Can I borrow this, Eliza?" he asked.

"What on earth for?"

"You'll see next time you come visiting," he answered as he ran down the steps.

As soon as he reached home he began to set up his business. First he twisted one end of the wire into a circle for a base and straightened the remaining five feet so that it would stand upright, a thin perpendicular spike beside his desk.

"Biggest spindle in town," he murmured. "And I'll need every inch of it."

He culled all his rejected manuscripts from his bureau drawers and the boxes under his bed and heaped them on the table. The mound was appalling, but he began at once on the ledger, recording the name of each story or article, the publishers to whom he had sent it, and the amount of postage he had used. Only a few of the first, worthless stories went into the wastebasket, but every rejection slip was impaled on the spindle.

The moon was out when he carried the debris of envelopes and worthless manuscripts to the trash can at the back of the lot and set a match to it. As the flames shot up, his only regret was for the waste of stamps.

Back in his room, Jack sorted the remaining manuscripts and planned where he would send them as soon as he could buy stamps.

I'll write a thousand words a day, he decided. Write slowly and think things through. The rest of the time I'll study and talk to people. I'm getting stale.

He thought of Jim Whitaker and some of the other men he'd met whose conversations always stimulated him to better work. And he needed some fun, the kind he used to have with the old crowd.

Bess must be lonely, too, he thought. Maybe we can have some bicycle trips together.

Later Jack was able to mark the day, July 29, 1899, when the new phase of his life really began, though it came innocently enough in a letter from the editor of the *Atlantic Monthly,* one of America's foremost magazines. A long story he had sent them, "An Odyssey of

226

the North," pleased them very much and they wished to publish it if he would cut out about three thousand words.

This is it! he thought. This is what I've been waiting for.

He jumped onto his old, wobbly bicycle and headed toward Bess Maddern's house, about a mile up Broadway from the center of town. Traffic thinned out quickly as he headed north, and he took the center of the wide dirt road where he could avoid the hard ruts.

First thing I'll do when I get my money is buy a new bicycle, he vowed, thinking of all the trips he and Bess had planned—a weekend at College Park with the Applegarths, a jaunt across the bay and the Golden Gate by ferry with their bicycles, to explore Mill Valley to the north. What fun they would have!

But I'll have to get a new wheel, he told himself impatiently as the old rusty chain clanked with every turn.

He dropped his wheel on the wide lawn at the corner of Twenty-fourth and Broadway, took the steps two at a time, and waved to Bess's mother who was, as usual, working among her plants and flowers in the glassed-in solarium beside the front door.

He rang the bell and pushed open the door, smiling to himself as he compared this comfortable big house with the fussy elegance of the Applegarth establishment. Nobody lifted an eyebrow if he raised his voice or arrived in his old clothes. This was a real home.

Bess came running down the stairs.

"Look," he said, as he thrust the letter into her hand.

He watched her face as she read it to the end. Her reaction was just what he had expected, an honest, straightforward one.

"That's fine, Jack," she said. "I'm so glad for you. You've worked hard and deserve it."

"Know what I'm going to do first thing when I get my money? I'll buy a new bicycle so we can take some real jaunts."

Her hazel eyes lit up and then sobered. "Can you afford it, do you think?"

"Sure!" He searched through his pockets again. "Guess I forgot the other letter from the *Arena*. They've accepted some old stuff about my tramp days that I've been sending around. And I'm hammering away at the *Youth's Companion*. You'll see." His confidence could not be dimmed now.

When he left Bess he scorched down to the library to tell Mr. Bamford, and then on to Alameda to give Jim Whitaker the word. On the way back he stopped at the First and Last Chance to let Johnny Heinold know that his investment had paid off. Back home he rushed, to write a long letter to Cloudesley Johns.

As the word filtered through Oakland that Jack London, that out-of-work fellow who was always broke, had sold a story to the *Atlantic Monthly,* all sorts of people began to drop in to see him. Old shipmates, returned Klondikers, tramps he had met on the road turned up. They told him what a wonderful fellow he was and always ended the conversation with a request for a loan. People he scarcely knew stopped him on the street to shake his hand. And the Oakland section of the Socialist Labor party, impressed with his success, asked him to deliver a speech.

At first the new attention was flattering and he enjoyed it, especially while checks were coming in from the most unexpected places for work that had been rejected again and again. Time was not so urgent, and he could spend it on people who sought him out.

When, in early September, the *Youth's Companion* sent thirty-five dollars for an article that he thought little of, he bought a new Cleveland bicycle and began the jaunts with Bess that they had planned, taking along a camera and developing the films in a darkroom at the Madderns' afterward. In October, when the *Atlantic* sent one hundred and twenty-five dollars, he bought his first typewriter, a new suit, and some white shirts with soft collars that would not cut his neck.

Still sure of himself, he sent the eight Klondike stories that had been published in the *Overland Monthly* plus "An Odyssey of the North" to the publishers Houghton, Mifflin and Company, with the suggestion that they be made into a book. For a while he refused to face the fact that everything he was submitting for publication had been written before his success with the *Atlantic*. I'm cleaning up my desk, he told himself proudly.

In December, when he was invited to address the

San Francisco Labor party meeting, his circle of acquaintances widened. Notices for the meeting billed him as "the distinguished magazine writer" and people flocked to hear him. Among them were some very intelligent, well-informed men and women who welcomed him into their group, and he began to spend many evenings in San Francisco listening to a kind of talk so stimulating that he was unable to settle down to work the next day.

In contrast to the past year, life was exciting and wonderful. But while he was enjoying it to the full, something warned him that it could not last. The conversations with his new friends proved how much he must read, how hard he must yet study. And the rapidly diminishing stack of saleable material on his desk told him daily that the time would come when he would have nothing more to sell.

On the first Monday morning in January, Jack's mother invaded his room and shook him as she had each morning when he was a boy.

"The grocer's cut us off again," she complained loudly.

Jack sat up in bed and hugged his knees. "All right, Ma. I'll talk to him."

"Talking won't do any good. He wants money."

Jack pulled himself from his warm bed and gazed out the window. It was already daylight. He had been out late the night before and was in no mood to argue with the grocer or anyone else.

In silence he ate his breakfast while his mother thumped around the kitchen. And then he went back to his room and opened his ledger.

There was no doubt about it—for a beginner only twenty-three years old, he had published a great deal during 1899. He counted the list. Twenty-four stories, articles, and poems! Except for the Klondike stories, it was mostly hack work, he knew, but it brought in much-needed cash.

Houghton, Mifflin and Company were preparing the Klondike stories for book publication sometime in March. *The Son of the Wolf* it would be called. But royalties would be a long time in coming. A few small pieces were in the mail, but they wouldn't bring in much. Meanwhile . . .

Jack reached into his pocket and brought out one dollar and some small change. He had spent his money as fast as it came in, he knew, but the demands had been heavy on him to dress well, go here and there, lend to out-of-luck friends.

I'll have to get in and dig, now, he told himself. Can't lose out when I've got a good start like this. Get back to my regular stint, maybe up it to fifteen hundred or two thousand words a day until I get things in running order again.

He pulled on his coat and went out into the kitchen to

face his irate mother. She was right. He'd been loafing on the job.

"I'm taking my new bicycle down to the pawnshop," he told her. "When I've paid the grocer and picked up a few stamps, I'll come back and get to work."

With the arrival of spring, Jack could stand his little ten-foot room no longer. Every inch of space was filled with books, manuscripts, notes, and letters. He could scarcely turn around.

Cloudesley Johns paid him a visit and had to share his bed. A wandering socialist friend who seemed to have no permanent home came often, talked late into the night, and stayed on to sleep. Other visitors crowded into his room when he was trying to work, driving him to distraction.

Why can't I live like other people? he fumed, whenever he had to pull a box from under the bed and search for notes that he needed.

He talked of going to Paris or of booking passage on a ship sailing around the Horn—anything to get away and stretch his wings for a while. But he was not serious. To go away now would be disastrous for his career.

What he really wanted, what he had wanted for a long time, was a home like some of those he had been invited to, with a nice living room in which he could entertain guests, a real dining room with a big table on which there would always be plenty of food to share, and a quiet study away from the kitchen, where he could work without hearing his mother's conversations with the neighbor women or the screaming of children in the next yard.

A pleasant home with a nice wife and children. I used to dream about that, he remembered.

Money was coming in more regularly now. The *Youth's Companion* and *McClure's* were paying well for his stories and asking for more. *Atlantic Monthly* wanted another.

On a Sunday in March, when he went bicycling with Bess, they found a two-story house about a mile farther east on Fifteenth Street near Twenty-third Avenue with a FOR RENT sign in the window. It was not elegant, but it seemed roomy, and they stopped to look.

As Jack wandered through the seven large rooms, saw an upstairs room nearly twice the size of his present one that could be his study, and the huge attic where he could store all his gear, he made up his mind at once. He must have it.

"Hate to think of all the confusion and the time lost with moving," he admitted to Bess as they left. "But I've got to do it. I can't stand that room any longer."

"I'll help," Bess offered. "You could get a carpenter to build some bookshelves. And maybe you could find a real desk in a secondhand store. You know—the big kind with pigeonholes for letters and a roll top!"

Bookshelves and a real desk! Living room. Dining room. Everything but a wife and children. Jack thought of Mabel Applegarth. For two years of his life he had

233

dreamed of sharing a home with her. But that was all in the past. Mabel would always try to make him into her image of the ideal man, and he had come to dislike the picture. As for children—she had never been strong.

Jack's mother was so excited over the idea of managing a big home for her son that he could not talk to her about the thoughts that kept running through his head. But all during the days of moving and getting settled, the idea of marriage kept recurring. Never before had he dared to consider it, except as something in the distant future. But now, with a big house and more money coming in . . .

I need to put out a sheet anchor, he told himself. Something to keep me steady in a storm. And Bess is just the one for me. She's got a level head.

He knew that she had been in love with Fred Jacobs and still spoke of him often; he knew that he was not really in love with her. But love's only a sentimental trick, he told himself. If I'd had the money, I might have married Mabel Applegarth. And then what a mess my life would have been! No, a fellow should use his head when he's making important decisions about his future. Besides, we always have such fun together.

That night, after Bess helped to arrange the books in his study, Jack talked to her for a long time. At last she agreed to marry him, and on the next Saturday, April 7, 1900.

Chapter 16

In the fall of 1901, Jack strolled down Broadway toward the library one afternoon to confer with Mr. Bamford about the next meeting of the Ruskin Club, of which he was now a member. The walk from his latest home, on Bayo Vista Avenue in the fashionable foothills area of Oakland, should not have taken very long. But every now and then someone stopped him to talk.

Occasionally he adjusted the flowing necktie and soft white collar of his expensive shirt, conscious that they were different from the stiff collars and narrow ties of other men, that they had become a symbol of his rugged individualism. They brought admiring glances from the women he passed on Broadway, many of whom had flocked to hear his lectures and gain an introduction to the well-known writer.

His lips twisted ironically, and then the corners of his full mouth drooped again into the unhappy expression that was becoming habitual. As though to prolong this trip that he really did not need to make, he paused now and then to gaze into store windows.

I could buy anything I want, he told himself. Walk right in and charge it in a minute. Suits. Hats. Neckties.

But now that he could have them, there was nothing he wanted.

In a candy store window, he gazed at the mounds of sweets, tastefully arranged on trays to tempt him. In the center was a glass jar filled with red-hots. *Nickel's worth of red-hots.* What had he ever seen in them?

Two small ragged boys stood with their noses pressed against the glass, their eyes feasting upon the wonders within. He looked at them and saw himself, ragged and hungry, mouth watering for what he could not have.

He reached into his pocket, pulled out two quarters, and handed one to each of the boys.

"Here," he said. "Get yourselves some candy."

The boys stared up at him, eyes wide in their pale faces.

"Gee, Mister. Thanks," they said as they scurried through the door.

Jack blinked the mist from his eyes as he turned away.

What's wrong with me? he asked himself. I've got everything I always wanted. A home, a fine little daughter, a good wife even if she is too busy with the house and baby to be much fun any more. Books, clothes, friends. And time. Everything I ever wanted.

236

He shook his head as he walked on toward the library. There was something wrong—terribly wrong. It was like a long sickness from which he could not seem to recover. He did not know what it was or how to cure it.

His life should have been good. It *was* good. Each morning, just as he had planned, he wrote his thousand words and outlined the next day's work. Then the time was his for writing letters, reading, and fencing or boxing with Jim Whitaker to keep in shape. Evenings were more than full with lectures, meetings, and dinner engagements.

Every Wednesday he held open house when his friends came for good talk and fun. The big dining room table was always loaded with food—Bess saw to that, even though the grocer must sometimes wait for his money. In the evenings they often played hilarious games while he hid his depression and tried to make up for some of the fun he had not had when he was a boy.

And yet, when the crowd left, when he faced the next day, the empty feeling came again.

Sometimes, in an attempt to cheer himself, he got out his ledger and counted his publications. Nearly fifty short stories, articles, and poems since his marriage! Pretty good for a twenty-five-year-old coal-shoveler, he would gloat to himself, as though the magic of numbers would make up for the fact that what he had written and published was chiefly hack work, written to pay for the things that he believed he wanted.

Jack stopped on the library steps, and as he had so often done, stared out toward the bay and the Golden Gate. And then he pushed open the library door to find Mr. Bamford and talk about the Ruskin Club meeting. This was a group of very respectable Oakland intellectuals who met each month in evening dress for dinner and a discussion of socialism. "Parlor Socialists" Jack often called them. But he had become a staunch member of the group.

As he walked up the stairs, however, his thoughts were still filled with the smell of the sea. Some day I'm going to cut loose, he promised himself again. Maybe get on a ship and travel around the world.

But now he could not do it. Though his ship was rocking badly, he had put out a sheet anchor to steady himself through just such a storm as this one.

The long sickness of discontent stayed with Jack through the first half of 1902, but few of his friends were allowed to know of it. While the old Socialist Labor party went through a stormy period to become the Social Democratic party he took little interest in the fight, though he always responded to increasing requests to write articles and make public speeches for the cause. He could say anything, now, and crowds would gather to hear him.

In February he moved his family again, this time to a large bungalow on five acres of land far up in the

Piedmont hills, removing himself even further from the people whom he wanted to avoid—the middle class people who, a few years ago, did not know that he existed but who now made demands upon him.

His chief satisfaction during this time was his little daughter, Joan, one year old on the fifteenth of January. When he played with her in the poppy-covered fields and took pictures of her to develop in his darkroom in the bungalow, he was happy. There were other satisfactions, too, like helping Jim Whitaker with monthly checks and advice until he, too, was selling stories to the best magazines.

But he was tied to the life that he had created for himself. There was no escape. Only by sitting down at his desk and hammering out his thousand words a day could he support his family and his mother. If he slackened, if the checks stopped coming, if his public grew tired of reading his red-blooded stories, the grocer would cut off his credit and he would be back where he started from.

I've roamed too much, he moaned to himself. Sailor, tramp, Klondiker. This settled life stifles me; I can't breathe.

On the twenty-first of July, 1902, while Jack was finishing the correction of proofs for his collection of Indian stories, *Children of the Frost,* to be published by The Macmillan Company, Bess came to his study door with a telegram. For only the most important matters did anyone disturb him at work, and he frowned as he ripped open the yellow envelope and read the contents.

But slowly the frown left his face and a faraway look took its place as he went over the message a second time. When he looked up, he avoided his wife's eyes.

"Have to leave for South Africa at once," he said. "The American Press Association wants me to write a series of articles on postwar conditions there."

"South Africa! What on earth for?"

"You must have heard that the Boer War is over," he snapped to cover his excitement at the thought of leaving. "They want me to go, that's all. Find out when the next train leaves for New York, will you? I'll have to send a wire that I'm coming at once."

Out of the corner of his eye, he saw Bess turn and leave the room. In a few months their second child would be born, perhaps this time the son that he longed for. He shouldn't leave, he knew.

But I *have* to get away, he told himself. Get a new grip on things before I settle down again to even more responsibilities.

The Overland Limited! Jack chuckled to himself as he sat in the dining car while servile waiters hovered over him, responding to his every wish. Wonder what they'd think if I told them how I rode this train the last time I crossed the country, eight years ago, he thought.

Bet they don't even know what a "side-door Pullman" is.

As the train sped along, he watched eagerly for the landmarks that he remembered. There was the place where the "shacks" had chased him from a blind three times. But I outsmarted 'em, he gloated. Farther along he spotted a barn where he was sure he had spent a night with the horses and cattle until a farmer routed him out at dawn.

When they pulled up into the mountains beyond Laramie, he leaned forward, scanning the tracks for the place where the refrigerator car filled with eighty-four members of the Nevada Push must have stood. But in that blinding snowstorm eight years before, no landmarks had been visible.

Jack leaned back in his seat, aware, suddenly, that his heart was pounding rapidly. He tried to laugh, knowing that his heart had not pounded like that for a long time.

Funny thing, he told himself. You look back and think of how cold and hungry and ragged you were, and all you can remember is how happy you were.

On the fourth day, when the train crossed the Missouri River bridge between Omaha, Nebraska, and Council Bluffs, Iowa, the picture came clearer. The corn was waist high now and the sweet smell of growing things drifted through his open window. Weston, Neola, Minden . . . They hadn't changed. All those kind people who had brought food to the roadside were probably still telling stories of the day when Kelley's Army marched through town. And as the train slowed for the station in Des Moines, there it was—the old stove works, just as dilapidated as it was in 1894!

Wonder what ever happened to Scotty and Boiler-maker and the others? he thought. Best fellows in the whole army.

And then he remembered where he was and who he was.

I'm getting sentimental now that I'm an old man of twenty-six, he told himself, trying to laugh off his excitement. But it stayed with him all the way to New York, starting up a whole new chain of thought.

If I were down in City Hall Park now, he decided, I'd see things in a different light. I'd talk to the people, find out more about them, how they live, what they think. Trouble with me is—I've been too far away from the people these last few years, writing, lecturing, going out in society all dressed up. I've lost touch.

By the time Jack got off the train in New York an idea had taken hold of him that put everything else into the shadows. His schedule, he believed, would allow him two days in England before the coronation of King Edward the Seventh, just time enough to disappear into the East End of London, the slums, and view the coronation from the point of view of the working class of a huge city—the class of people he had seen in New York's lower East Side. What a story that would make!

As soon as he got off the train, he hurried to the office of The Macmillan Company to talk with the editor, George Brett, about it. This would be just the sort of thing that would appeal to him.

At the end of the first week of August, Jack stood before the mirror in a room that he had rented in North London, and swiftly began to change himself from successful writer to an American sailor who had spent his money and was temporarily broke while looking for another ship, for that was the role that he had decided to play. He took off his soft gray suit and comfortable shoes and unrolled a bundle of garments that he had bought in an old-clothes shop in Petticoat Lane the day before. Then he pulled on the old trousers, the harsh stoker's shirt, and the frayed jacket with only one remaining button. After pounding the stiff leather of the old shoes with his fists, he managed to soften them enough so that he could force his feet into them. With a cringe, he settled the dirty cap onto his head, and was ready to leave.

"Blimy, yer a sight, ain't ya," he chortled to the character he saw in the mirror.

He hid some money in the sleeve of his jacket, stuffed a few shillings, a knife, and a handkerchief into his pocket, and clumped down the stairs and out into the rain, heading for the East End of London that he had viewed from a hansom cab the day before.

At first he felt self-conscious, but in a few minutes

he realized that no one was paying any attention to him at all. The day before, dressed in his fine clothes, people had stood aside, addressing him as "governor" or "sir." But now he found that he had to step more lively when crossing streets, to avoid the vehicles that crowded the narrow thoroughfares.

He had been in London only two days, but the events of those two days were already far in the back of his thoughts. First, the cable from the American Press Association, canceling their plans for his South African series. With a ticket home and some money in his pocket, he received the news with little regret, for the story he wanted to write was uppermost in his mind. There followed the finding of a simple room in North London where he could write, the visit to the American consul-general, to whom he identified himself and explained his plans, in case he should run into trouble. And last, the trip through the East End by hansom so that he could see what it was like and, of course, buy clothes that would not make him conspicuous there.

As Jack moved deeper into the slum area of the huge city, the rolling gait of Sailor Jack came back into his stride. He was one of the crowd, now, but as he looked around he began to feel as though he were among people of a different race. Their stunted bodies and wretched appearance appalled him.

In a narrow, filthy alley he watched old men and women claw through garbage dumped in the slime of the streets, saw children dig their arms into rotten fruit and cram bits of it into their hungry mouths.

I thought New York City was bad, he remembered, but I didn't see anything like this.

His stomach revolted, but he turned up his collar and moved on, reminding himself that he was here to observe and write, not to try to change things.

The farther he walked, the denser became the crowds of wretched people who seemed to have no homes. They stood in doorways, leaned against the leeward sides of buildings, or shuffled along in the drenching rain.

At Whitechapel Workhouse, Jack stood in the crowd waiting at the door, striking up a conversation with two small, shivering older men. One had been a carter, he learned, and the other a carpenter. But there was no work for them now. When the call "full up," came from the door, the three turned away together.

"Poplar Workhouse," the carter groaned. "Not much of a show, but we'd best chance it. I'm fagged out. My legs is hurtin' me somethin' fearful."

As they walked up Mile End Road, the men, taking him for what he said he was, a down-in-luck sailor, confided their woes to him. One had been on the streets for five nights; the other for three. One had had a small hard roll that day; the other nothing. As Jack asked questions and they answered, he noticed that they kept their eyes on the street, and to his horror he watched them pick up all sorts of things and put them into their mouths: bits of orange peel, apple skins, blackened apple cores, seeds, tiny crumbs of bread . . .

The workhouse, if they could get in, would give them six ounces of bread and a cup of "skilly," a little oatmeal mixed with hot water, he learned. After a like breakfast in the morning they must spend the day at labor— locked in a room picking oakum or breaking rock. One day was all they would be allowed; the following morning they would be put out on the streets again.

At Poplar Workhouse, where they again heard "full up," Jack could stand it no longer. He pulled out the money he had hidden and took the men into a coffee house where he treated them to all the eggs and bacon, bread and tea that they could eat. When he left them with a couple of shillings each he hurried back to his room in North London to write through the night of the things he had seen and heard.

The few days that Jack had intended to spend in London stretched into seven weeks. In his ragged clothes he mingled with the people of the social abyss, listened to their stories, and sat for hours afterward in his room writing . . . writing . . . Sometimes at night he walked near the locked gates of the parks in the fashionable West End of London with the homeless people, never permitted by the police to sit down until daylight. At dawn when the gates were unlocked, he went with them into Hyde Park or Green Park and watched them throw themselves onto the benches or even the rain-drenched grass to sleep away their exhaustion.

Toward the end of his stay, Jack took pictures of the workhouses, the people, the old women in the parks to verify his story. He gathered statistics, and was overwhelmed to learn what a great percentage of the people of the huge city died of poverty or lived their lives on the very edge of starvation. And this year, 1902, was a good year, he was told.

What good is civilization, he asked himself, if it can't better the lot of the average man? Even the Indians of Alaska, in their mud huts, are better off. At least they have fuel and shelter. And only in the bad times is there starvation. Here, in this great civilized city, hunger and misery are chronic things.

When Jack finished the last of his sixty-thousand-word manuscript, *The People of the Abyss,* he was worn out by what he had seen and experienced of economic degradation. But in his heart he felt good about what he had done. He had uncovered the truth and had written about it for seven weeks, without once counting his thousand words a day or thinking of how much he would earn by the labor of his pen.

Now his thoughts turned toward California and the clean, airy home in the poppy fields, to his family and friends from whom he had wanted to get away. For a few weeks, while he made a short trip through France, Germany, and Italy, he wrote often to Bess, the only love letters she ever received from him. When a cable reached him saying that a second daughter, Bess, had been born, he booked passage at once for home.

In New York he stopped briefly to deliver *The People of the Abyss* to his enthusiastic publisher and talk of the sea story that he wanted to write. Mr. Brett offered to advance him one hundred and fifty dollars each month so that he could work without financial pressure, and he accepted gratefully.

No more hack work, he told himself. No more drudgery.

The train could not go fast enough for Jack as he headed west, all his thoughts now on reaching home. When at last he held Joan in his arms and looked upon the tiny baby that was his second daughter, he was content.

"This is the most wonderful place in the world," he said to Bess as they stood arm in arm on the veranda of the bungalow and looked out over the whole sweep of the bay and the Golden Gate. "Whenever I come back to it, I always wonder why in the world I ever wanted to leave. You have no idea how I'll be able to work now. I'm going to write that sea story that I've been wanting to do for a long time."

But when he sat down to his desk, for some reason that he could not understand, a far different story kept crowding into his thoughts. Why it would not leave him in peace to carry out his agreement with Mr. Brett, he did not know. But there it was, day and night.

I might as well go ahead and write it, he finally decided. It shouldn't take more than a few days; four thousand words ought to be enough. It'll be just another dog story; I don't know why I'm so excited about it.

In a camp near Dawson he had seen a fine, sensitive dog named Buck that he had never been able to forget. At one time he must have been someone's pet. Probably he was one of the many dogs stolen from the streets of West Coast cities and shipped to the Yukon during the early months of the gold rush. Under the law of club and fang, many dogs had died. But this one, scarred though he was, had come through.

Jack's imagination went further, carrying this creature of civilization into the wildest regions of the Yukon where, by his own strength and courage, he would survive to lead the pack.

Eagerly Jack set to work, but by the time he had written four thousand words, he knew that he had only begun and that it was gripping his imagination as no other story had. He shut himself into his room and wrote on and on, forgetting to count words, forgetting everything except Buck and his inevitable response to the call of the wild.

As the story progressed Jack knew that he was writing better than he had ever written before. After weeks of describing the filth of slums, he was escaping into a land of primitive beauty unspoiled by civilization, that was a joy to describe. Buck, moving fearlessly toward his destiny, was a creature after his own heart. His was the everlasting struggle of the strong to survive, a struggle that Jack knew so well.

In a month he finished his story, *The Call of the Wild,*

and counted the words. Thirty-two thousand! What would George Brett think? He sent one copy to the *Saturday Evening Post* and another to his publisher, and turned at once to the sea story.

Several months later, when *The Call of the Wild* appeared in the bookstores, following serialization in the *Saturday Evening Post,* the first edition of ten thousand copies was gone in a day. Further editions were bought up as fast as they were issued. Critics and reviewers gave it the highest praise, and flattering letters poured into the bungalow in Piedmont.

But of all the people who read the reviews and listened to the praise, no one was more surprised and bewildered than the author himself. What had he done to deserve such loud applause, the kind that he had only dreamed of having some day? Why was this story better than anything he had written before?

To his clamoring public, he declared that the success of the book was merely a matter of luck. But alone, in the dark hours of the night, he searched for the answer in all the months of struggle that had brought him to this point.

During the past year, release from the hack work that he had come to hate had given him time to write of things that stirred his heart. In *The People of the Abyss,* the poor and the hungry were real and tragic; he had once been poor and hungry, too. And his dog story? The

250

reviewers said that it was a human allegory. With human beings as with animals, the struggle for survival was the same. Buck's struggle? Or was it his own that he had been writing about?

That must be the answer, he concluded. I used to think I knew everything there was to know about the writing business. I learned the words, studied the other writers, hammered out my thousand words a day, and kept a ledger. But that wasn't enough. I left out the most important thing—some of my own heart and blood, a part of myself.

POSTSCRIPT

The Call of the Wild and *The Sea Wolf* established Jack London as one of the most popular writers of his day. With these books he proved to himself and to the world that he had the talent and ability to write enduring fiction.

But the habits of his life were strong. From the day when he had decided to develop his brains and sell them for financial security and all the things that money could buy, he had never ceased striving toward that end. Now, though he often told himself and his friends that some day he would be free to write the great stories that were in him, he continued to pour out chiefly the red-blooded fiction that his public demanded and that paid so well. He drove himself almost beyond the limits of human endurance, sometimes publishing as many as four books in one year, besides many short stories and articles, working too fast and refusing to rewrite or polish his work. Some of the stories were very good and some were poor. But the size of the check meant more to him than the quality of his writing.

When, in 1903, restlessness came upon him again, it was his settled life that he blamed. He left his wife and daughters permanently, though he always provided for them during his lifetime and saw them whenever he was in Oakland. Searching now more frantically for the happiness that always eluded him, he married again, this time a member of the new group of admirers, Charmian Kittredge.

Forgetting the satisfaction that he had found when he took up the cause of the working class and strove to better conditions for the underprivileged people of the world, he began a series of grandiose undertakings that only separated him further from them. At great cost he built a forty-five-foot sailing boat, the *Snark,* in which he intended to make a seven year voyage around the world with his new wife. But everything went wrong, and he returned in two years to California, deeply in debt and very ill.

Now he decided to build an immense home on land that he had purchased north of San Francisco, on the side of Sonoma Mountain overlooking the Valley of the Moon. For three years he wrote steadily to pay for it. Built of native stone and redwood, Wolf House would last for a thousand years, he said, but it burned to the ground the night before he was to move in. Only the huge shell of the red-brown stone remained to remind him of the impermanence of material things.

To the end of his life, Jack London was unable to resolve the conflicts within himself and therefore to find happiness and contentment. He was like two different people. One was the warmhearted person who wrote articles without thought of payment in which he deplored the system that did not allow the kind of people whom he had grown up with to have a decent standard of living. Always openhanded, he gave to every needy person who asked for help, and took great pains to help many beginning writers. But the other person who was Jack London, the highest paid writer in America, lived in grand style on his huge ranch apart from the world and wondered why he was lonely.

Perhaps the need to understand what had gone wrong with his plan made him sometimes write about himself. "I was Martin Eden," he said of the leading character in one of his best books, a novel named *Martin Eden*. Before his death, when the need became stronger, he was planning a series of autobiographical books. But he did not live to write them and did not learn the answer.

On November 22, 1916, at the age of forty, deeply depressed, ill and often in great pain, he died from an overdose of morphine. As he wished, only a large boulder of native stone marks his grave near the ruins of Wolf House.

SOURCES

Like others who have written about Jack London, I have relied most heavily upon two works: *Jack London and His Times* by Joan London, Doubleday, Doran and Company, Inc., New York, 1939; *The Book of Jack London,* two volumes, by Charmian London, The Century Company, New York, 1921.

Other publications that have been especially helpful are:

Jack London, American Rebel by Philip S. Foner. Citadel Press, New York, 1947.

The Mystery of Jack London by Georgia Loring Bamford. Privately published, Oakland, California, 1931.

The Palimpsest (containing a Jack London diary). The State Historical Society of Iowa, Iowa City, May, 1926.

The Klondike Fever by Pierre Berton. Alfred A. Knopf, Inc., New York, 1958.

Klondike '98, Hegg's Album of the 1898 Gold Rush by Ethel Anderson Becker. Binfords and Mort, Portland, Oregon, 1958.

Jack London wrote so many articles and stories about his experiences in all parts of the world that it is impractical to list them here. Those of particular significance to the years covered in this book are: "What Life Means to Me," 1906; *The Road,* 1907; *Martin Eden,* 1909; and *John Barleycorn,* 1913.

In a class by itself but no less important to any London biographer is the remarkable Knowland Collection of enlarged photographs that line the corridor walls of the Oakland Public Library. Many scenes and events of Oakland, California, at the turn of the century are pictured there.

One of my great pleasures in writing this book has derived from the kindness of people unknown to me before I began it—the strangers who offered their valuable London collections for my use; the librarians who cheerfully searched through old directories for some small scrap of information that I could not do without. To all who have helped me in any way, large or small, I am most grateful.

But to Joan London Miller I am especially indebted. She has given unstintingly from her knowledge of her father, opening doors for me that might have been forever closed, sharing books and photographs and descriptions from her memory. The warm friendship that has grown from our association is gratifying indeed.

Index

London, John (father), 11, 12, 13, 14, 31, 56
  death of, 206
  and fishing, 5, 8
  and Gold Rush, 179
  illness of, 169
  and Jack's writing, 40
  and Kelley's Army, 64–66
  and work, 9, 16, 17, 47–48, 98
London, Bess Maddern (the first Mrs. Jack London), *see* Maddern, Bess
London, Charmian Kittredge (the second Mrs. Jack London), 254
Lucky Swede, 200

McChesney, Principal, 102–103, 140
McClure's, 233
McPhee, Bill, 200

Macmillan Co., 239, 243, 248, 250
Maddern, Bess (first Mrs. Jack London), 133, 154, 226, 227, 229, 248
  at concert, 124–126

262

Maddern, Bess (*cont.*)
  and education, 129–130, 136, 144, 152, 158–159
  influence of, 158–159
  and Jack's writing, 228, 239–240
  and Jacobs, Fred, 209
  marriage of, 233, 234, 237, 239–240, 247, 254
  meeting with, 115–116, 124–126
Maddern, Mrs., 227
mail carrier job, 211, 212–213, 217, 223–224
Maine, 206
Mane of the Horse Rapids, 195
Martin Eden, 255
Melville, Herman, 60
Mikado, 9
Miles Canyon, 192–194
Miller, Joan London, *see* London, Joan
Murphy, Bill, 156

Nevada Push, 71 ff., 241
New York, 79–85
Niagara Falls, 85–89

Oakland High School, 102–107, 110–111, 140

About the Author

As with her previous books—Willa: The Story of Willa Cather's Growing Up *and* Stephen Crane: The Story of an American Writer—*Ruth Franchere spent many months of intensive research before beginning* Jack London. *She traveled up and down the West Coast, talking with people who knew London and searching into old newspapers and records. Days of investigation at the public library in Oakland, California, were followed by evenings of discussion with London's daughter, Joan. Mrs. Franchere was determined to present not only the facts of Jack London's life, but the emotions and the environment which made that life one of the most interesting in our literary history.*

Mrs. Franchere, a native of Mason City, Iowa, was graduated from the University of Iowa and has taught English composition at several colleges and universities. Her husband, Hoyt C. Franchere, is chairman of the Division of Humanities at Portland State College. The Francheres live in Portland, Oregon, and have a married daughter, Julie.